GREAT LIVES IN BRIEF
A New Series of Biographies

ACCURACY
BREVITY CLARITY
MULTUM
IN PARVO

These are
BORZOI BOOKS
Published by ALFRED A. KNOPF
in New York

CHARLES DARWIN

Charles Darwin

A GREAT LIFE IN BRIEF

BY

Ruth Moore

New York   ALFRED A. KNOPF   1955

L. C. catalog card number: 54–7221

THIS IS A BORZOI BOOK,
PUBLISHED BY ALFRED A. KNOPF, INC.

FIRST EDITION

CONTENTS

CHARLES DARWIN

ONE

THE EMINENTLY CURIOUS GALÁPAGOS

FROM the ocean the islands seemed to be only a mass of craters; the flanks of the big symmetrical central cones were pocked with innumerable smaller orifices.

When H.M.S. *Beagle* came to anchor on the morning of September 17, 1835 and the ship's young naturalist, Charles Darwin, went ashore, his first closer impression was that "nothing could have been less inviting than the strange cyclopean landscape." The shore of Chatham Island, the easternmost of the ten larger islands of the Galápagos Archipelago, was a broken field of black lava, tossed into the most rugged waves and crossed by great fissures. Stunted, sunburned brushwood nearly covered the dry, parched surface, and in the sultry heat of noonday "the wretched looking little weeds" even seemed to give off an acrid, evil smell. And on the black rocks bordering the sea huge black lizards dozed in the sun.

There was nothing in Charles Darwin's first glimpse of the Galápagos to tell him that these remote mid-Pacific islands would go far toward upsetting all that he and the world then believed about the origin of all living things on this earth.

The *Beagle*, a ten-gun brig, had sailed from England on December 27, 1831 to complete a survey of some of the world's lesser-known waters and to carry a chain of chronometrical measurements around the world.

Captain Robert Fitzroy, the ship's young commander,

had wanted a young man "qualified to examine the land" to go along on the voyage, and had invited Charles Darwin, then twenty-two and only recently out of Cambridge, to accept the unpaid post.

As the *Beagle* sailed her rough and often stormy way across the Atlantic and up and down the coasts of South America, her eager, newly made naturalist collected everything that came to his hand or attracted his discerning eye—marine specimens, an African cricket that landed on the ship when it was three hundred and seventy miles from the African coast, and animals, insects, reptiles, plants, stones, and fossils from the shores, the mountains, the plains, and the fresh and salt waters of South America.

Charles Darwin was a born collector suddenly presented with the whole world in which to collect. More than this, he had an amazing gift for seeing things as they were instead of as they were reputed to be, and a mind that constantly reached out for the total meanings that elude most men.

As the *Beagle* slowly made her way around the world, Darwin was struck by the curious likenesses and the curious dissimilarities of the specimens he gathered. The same haunting relationships were there whether the specimens came from the peaks of the Andes or the plains of the pampas, from the heart of a continent or from a tiny mid-ocean island.

If each of the multitude of species had been separately created as he and nearly all others thought in those early days of the nineteenth century, then why, he asked himself, did the mice he collected on the east side of the Andes differ from and yet resemble those he had captured on the west side of the great mountain barrier?

Why had closely allied animals replaced one another as he had moved southward from Brazil into Patagonia, and into the dense, gloomy forests of Tierra del Fuego? Why did living things vary as they did? And why were the huge fossil animals he dug from the pampean mud covered with armor very like that of living armadillos?

Early in the voyage a daring explanation had begun to form in Darwin's mind. If each species of man, or mouse, or armadillo, had not been separately created, but had evolved from some earlier form, the unexplainable might be explained. And if the lands and waters had risen and fallen and changed positions as he saw they had, it might be possible to account for life's being distributed around the earth in the way it was.

The tall, gray-eyed young Englishman to whom these nearly incredible ideas came was deeply modest. He was neither a rebel against the long-accepted beliefs of the past, nor a man to rush to beckoning new conclusions. He did not hasten to record these probing questions and ideas in the notebooks and the journal that he kept throughout the voyage. It is likely that Charles Darwin did not fully admit even to himself that he was forming a new and dangerously challenging concept of life's origins.

But many acts indicate that from an early stage of the voyage some of the critical points of his famous theory were tentatively in his mind. Was the odd little fish he caught in the net he towed behind the *Beagle* unique? Had the upthrusting of a mountain range halted the movements of animals, and had different species developed behind the barriers? Did the invader with a favorable edge drive out the old and long-established? By the time the *Beagle* reached the Galápagos, three years and nine months after the start of the voyage, all of Darwin's questions were within this framework. And yet he still was only questioning, only noting what his eyes would not permit him to miss. But his preparation had been excellent; he was uniquely ready for the startling surprises the Galápagos held in store.

On that hot September morning when Charles Darwin clambered up the rugged shores of Chatham Island, he was hoping and planning, as he always was when the *Beagle* reached any new land, to collect at least one specimen of every living thing. He decided that here he would begin with "botanizing." He soon saw, however, that on these sere, lava-scorched islands there were very few varieties of plants. The few, Darwin thought with a combination of disappointment and surprise, "might better have become an arctic than an equatorial flora." Darwin stopped to think; he could understand why—although the Galápagos lay directly below the equator, the cold waters of the south polar current that swirled around them kept the climate and the flora from being tropical.

It was not long before Darwin's first feeling of disappointment began to give way before a number of astonishing and interesting facts. The scrubby brushwood, which at first sight had looked as bare as an English oak in winter, actually was in full leaf and flower. The leaves were wretched, scrawny little things, and Darwin could not find "one beautiful flower," but he realized with a start that never before had he seen anything even resembling these peculiar plants, unless it was the vegetation on the Atlantic volcanic island of Fernando de Noronha. Here was something different. Darwin's interest leaped up; his disappointment vanished.

The *Beagle* sailed on around Chatham. While the ship anchored in one of the many bays for some survey work, Darwin pitched a tent on shore and began to explore farther inland. The going was not easy. From his camp he could count sixty red slag craters, nearly all of them fifty to one hundred feet high, and there were numberless steep-sided holes. The latter had been produced by the collapse of the "bubbles" that had welled up in the once fluid crust of the island.

The day was glowing hot, and scrambling around over this jagged terrain and through the thick brushwood would have been exhausting if Darwin had not been so buoyed up and absorbed by the strangeness of the scene. As he pushed on he suddenly came upon a well-beaten path. On an uninhabited island such as this, he realized at once, it must have been made by some animal. He did not have long to wonder. Around a bend he came upon two huge tortoises, two of the famous *galápagos* that had given the islands their name. One, which must have weighed two hundred pounds, was eating a piece of cactus. As Darwin came nearer, it stared at him and calmly ambled away. The other, almost as large, gave a deep hiss and drew in its head. The giant reptiles were no more alarmed at this intruder than were the dull-colored birds hopping about in the bush.

"These huge reptiles, surrounded by the black lava, the leafless shrubs and the large cacti, seemed to my fancy like some antediluvian animals," Darwin wrote in the journal that he faithfully kept.

The young English naturalist was fascinated. As the *Beagle* visited other islands and Darwin met more of the great imperturbable tortoises, a thought came to him which was only slightly less fantastic than his fancy that

the reptiles might have belonged to another world or
inhabited a different planet. The big tortoises, Darwin
noted in his journal, were "aboriginal"; they must have
originated on these islands. There clearly were no others
like them anywhere else in the world.

As far as anyone knew, the tortoises had always been
on the Galápagos Islands. The first buccaneers who put
into the islands had found them there in vast numbers,
and a scientific report had been made on them as early
as 1708. Constant hunting by the people of the islands
and by the crews of visiting ships had reduced their numbers by the time the *Beagle* arrived, but even so the
Beagle's crew captured fifteen in one day. A tale was
told of one vessel that had carried away seven hundred
and of the crew of a frigate that killed two hundred in
one day. For ships hungry for fresh meat, the tortoise
was a prize.

While the *Beagle* went off for water, Darwin and his
servant camped for a week on James Island. As he ex-
plored inland, Darwin soon discovered that the methodi-
cal tortoise paths led to springs in the high central part
of the island. There low-hanging clouds supplied moisture and turned the barren earth into a verdant green.
At the springs the big reptiles buried their heads in the
water and swallowed great mouthfuls. Darwin, always
the observant scientist, counted; they gulped down the
cool water at the rate of ten mouthfuls a minute.

Darwin also timed the tortoises on their journey.
They walked sixty yards in ten minutes and three hundred and sixty yards in an hour. This made four miles
in a day, and like the tortoise in the fable they plugged
steadily on day and night. The Spaniards said that they
were deaf, and this seemed to be true. As Darwin paced

along beside them they took no notice until he passed them by. At the moment they saw him they would draw in their heads and feet and with a sibilant hiss "fall to the ground as if struck dead." Darwin could not resist the opportunity this offered. He would climb on a tortoise's back and give a few raps on the hinder part of the shell, and his strange steed would rise and begin its slow walk. Keeping his seat was another matter; after a few steps the long-legged young English rider usually found himself sliding off.

Darwin's observations only increased his conviction: "There can be little doubt that the tortoise is an aboriginal inhabitant of the Galápagos."

As Darwin excitedly continued his explorations, he found that all about him were other aboriginal forms. Nowhere else in the world were there lizards like the three- and four-foot-long specimens that lay sunning themselves on the coastal rocks. The big yellowish-brown lizards that lived in the hills also were unique.

Early travelers had told of seeing the black aquatic lizards going to sea "in herds a-fishing." Charles Darwin too watched them going to sea, swimming through the water with a serpentine movement of their body and flattened tail, but he did not take it for granted that they were "a-fishing." He opened the stomachs of several and found them distended with a seaweed that grew on the sea bottom rather than on the tidal rocks. It could only mean that they were herbivorous, an observation confirmed by the fact that they had the large intestines typical of herbivorous animals. Darwin was amazed. A lizard that lived on marine vegetable productions was unheard of; no other did.

Everything—their food, their structure, and actual

observation—proved their aquatic habits, and yet there was one anomaly. When frightened, they would not enter the water.

Darwin established this to his own satisfaction and amusement. He chased some of the lizards down to a little point overhanging the water, and as he had seen, they refused to plunge in. Darwin picked one up by the tail and threw it into a deep pool left by the tide. Swimming near the bottom with a rapid, graceful movement, it returned in a direct line to the spot where he stood. As it crawled out and started to shuffle away, Darwin took it by the tail and heaved it in again. Again it came back. Each time Darwin repeated the performance the lizard returned, almost like a trained retriever. Pondering this odd action, Darwin thought it might be explained by the fact that the lizard had no enemies on shore, though at sea it must often have fallen prey to sharks. Hence, he reasoned, it probably made for the shore in an emergency of any kind.

The ugly yellow terrestrial species was so numerous on James Island that the *Beagle* party had difficulty finding a spot free of their burrows where a tent could be pitched. Walking was difficult too, for the men's feet always were sinking into the lizard warrens.

Darwin was almost as entertained by this group as by his seagoing comebacks. For hours he sat watching one dig its burrow. With one front leg it would dig up the soil and toss it toward its hind leg, which then heaved it out beyond the mouth of the hole. When that side tired, the lizard shifted to the other. When the lizard had about half of its body buried, Darwin walked up and pulled it by the tail.

"At this it was greatly astonished," he reported, "and

soon shuffled up to see what was the matter; and then stared me in the face as much as to say 'What made you pull my tail?' "

In the dry lower country in which the lizards lived there was almost no water. Evidently they got both moisture and nourishment from the succulent leaves of the cactus. Many times Darwin broke off a piece and tossed it to them. They would seize it in their mouths and run off with it, like dogs with a bone. The tame little birds also were fond of the cactus and would pick at one end of a piece while a lizard nibbled at the other.

As amusing as the lizards were, it was another fact about them that set Darwin to thinking long and questioningly. To find both the marine and terrestrial species of so well-characterized a genus in so confined a portion of the world was remarkable. He could not believe that so much "creative force" would have been lavished on such a small part of the globe. It stretched coincidence too far.

Another important question was presented by the lizards and the other reptiles of the Galápagos. Remembering the well-beaten paths made by the thousands of tortoises, the spreading warrens of the terrestrial lizards, and the colonies of the marine species, Darwin marveled at the way the reptiles had taken over the islands. Here they occupied the place in the economy of nature ordinarily held by the mammals. Nowhere else in the world had Darwin seen anything comparable. He again had a sense, he said, of having been carried back to an ancient era when lizards, some herbivorous and some carnivorous, and some of the dimensions of whales, swarmed dominatingly over land and sea.

Nor were the reptiles alone in their oddity, as though

they were the fanciful whim of some creator. The same unique pattern was to be seen in the birds and the other life of the archipelago. As Darwin wrote in his journal, the whole natural history of the islands was "eminently curious."

The young naturalist obtained twenty-six kinds of land birds, all peculiar to the islands and found nowhere else, with the exception of one far-ranging lark-like finch from North America. The Galápagos hawk was oddly intermediate between a buzzard and the American group of carrion-feeding Polybori, with which it agreed closely in its habits and even in its tone of voice. The islands also had a wren, three tyrant flycatchers, and a dove, all analogous to but distinct from the American species, and a "most singular group of finches." The finches were clearly related, though they formed thirteen distinct species, all peculiar to the archipelago. When Darwin arranged them in a series, he saw that their beaks graduated perfectly in size from a large parrot-like beak similar to that of the hawfinch to one as small and fine as that of the chaffinch.

"One might almost fancy that from an original paucity of birds in this archipelago, one species had been taken and modified for different ends," said Darwin, fleetingly touching on the suggestion that one species might have evolved into many, and yet not quite giving credence to the shocking idea.

Darwin was able to collect only eleven kinds of water waders and water birds, of which only three were new Galapageian species. This did not surprise him, for he understood even then that water birds were more widely distributed around the earth than land birds. In fact, he dared to refer to the law that "aquatic forms, whether marine or fresh water are less peculiar at any given point on the earth's surface than the terrestrial forms." With their ability to live on the water, aquatic birds could more easily make their way around a water-encircled world. They were more mobile.

The same law held true for the shells. Darwin collected sixteen kinds of fresh-water shells, all of which, with one exception, were peculiar to the Galápagos. Only forty-seven of the ninety known sea shells in the islands were unduplicated species, though to find forty-seven unique species was a "wonderful fact, considering how widely distributed sea shells are."

There were other facts about the shells to give pause to a naturalist who was continuing to ask why so much peculiarity should have been concentrated in one remote group of islands. Of the forty-three shells that also existed in other parts of the world, twenty-five inhabited the western coast of America and the others the Philippines or other Pacific areas. Surely this could only mean that some of them had come from the Pacific and some from the coast of America. Darwin's eager mind raced on. He knew—the books told him—that not a single sea shell was believed to be common to the Pacific islands and the coast of America. Each of these areas had its own distinctive species.

"The space of open sea running north and south off the west coast (of the Americas) separates two quite distinct conchological provinces; but at the Galapagos we have a halting place where many forms have been created and whither these two great conchological provinces have each sent several colonists," Darwin wrote in his journal.

In its birds, its reptiles, its water life, the archipelago

was zoologically a part of America, though the islands
stood alone in the heart of the Pacific more than five
hundred or six hundred sea miles removed from the nearest American land.

If the species had been exactly the same as those of
the Americas, there would have been little problem.
Then it would have been easy to assume that the American animals had somehow found a way to migrate to the
islands. But as he tramped around the islands, Darwin
kept reminding himself that more than half the plants
and many of the animals were "aboriginal," so different
from those of the Americas that they had to be classified
as different species, and yet they resembled the life of the
Americas.

"It was most striking," Darwin wrote, "to be surrounded by new birds, new reptiles, new shells, new insects, new plants, and yet by innumerable trifling details
of structure, and even by the tones of voice and the
plumage of the birds to have the temperate plains of
Patagonia or the hot deserts of Northern Chile brought
vividly before my eyes."

And there were other unavoidable questions. Why
were these strange inhabitants of the Galápagos associated in proportions different both in kind and in number from those in which their equivalents were found
on the continent? To ask these questions, to comprehend
the problem, was to seek an answer. As his journal
shows, the problem was constantly in Darwin's mind as
the *Beagle* lingered in the archipelago. But one all-
important clue came most unexpectedly.

Darwin was talking to a Vice Governor about the
tortoises. The island official remarked casually that the
tortoises from the various islands differed so much that

he could tell from which island any one of them came. The remark almost slipped by Darwin. Only some minutes later did its meaning and significance dawn on him. It had never occurred to Darwin that similar volcanic islands only fifty or sixty miles apart and within easy sight of one another could be differently tenanted. But the Vice Governor had said that he could distinguish between the tortoises, and that could only mean that they were different.

The *Beagle's* stay of a little more than a month was drawing to a close and there was tantalizingly little time in which to investigate this crucial point, but Darwin hurried to check it in so far as he could. His collections of tortoises from the various islands had been mixed together, and, by chance, contained mostly young animals in which the differences were not conspicuous. By some rapid though careful inquiring Darwin learned that the tortoises from Charles Island and from Hood, which stood very near to it, had thick shells which turned up in the front like Spanish saddles. Those from James Island were rounder and blacker and, Darwin was told, "have a better taste when cooked." The Vice Governor had been right.

Could other life differ from island to island? Darwin quickly began to examine other animals and plants that he had collected. Fortunately he had tagged each mocking thrush that he and other members of the *Beagle* party had shot with the name of the island on which it was taken.

To his "astonishment" he discovered that all the thrushes from Charles Island belonged to one species, and all from James and Chatham islands, between which there were two small connecting islands, to another.

His plants showed corresponding differences. Darwin had gathered everything in flower on the islands, and again had fortunately kept his collections separate. Thus he learned "the truly remarkable fact" that thirty of the distinctive Galapageian species of plants were confined to James Island.

Darwin thought his way carefully and tentatively toward the meaning of this amazing distribution of living things.

"It is the circumstance that several of the islands possess their own species of the tortoise, mocking thrush, finches and numerous plants, these species having the same general habits, occupying analogous situations and obviously filling the same place in the natural economy that strikes me with wonder," he said.

The young naturalist repeatedly asked himself how "these many peculiar animals and plants" could have been produced. He was far from ready to believe that he had the answer, and yet he saw with increasing clarity what it might be. If the inhabitants of the several islands had descended from each other, and had undergone modification in the course of their descent, the puzzling likenesses and differences could be understood. And if the first colonists had come from America, it would be possible to see why their descendants, though much changed, should still bear an American stamp.

How the modification might have been effected seemed at first an insoluble problem. But Darwin had already noticed in South America that where there was separation, when there was division, differences generally appeared. With growing excitement Darwin realized that the Galápagos Islands, in sight of one another though they were, were as effectively separated in some cases as though a wide ocean washed between them or a towering mountain chain divided them.

Between the northern and southern islands of the archipelago ran strong sea currents. All the chances were that any egg or seed falling into the water or any animal venturing into the swift currents would be swept out to sea rather than be landed safely on another of the islands. Nor was it likely that birds or seeds or insects would be blown from one island to the next, for the islands were remarkably free of gales. Lastly, the profound depth of the ocean between the islands, and their newness in the geologic sense, made it unlikely that they had ever been united.

In his journal Darwin made a note: the evidence of separation was the only light that he could throw on the puzzle of the strange, unique Galápagos species. He added: "One is astonished at the amount of creative force, if such an expression may be used, displayed on these small, barren and rocky islands, and still more so at its diverse yet analogous action on points so near each other."

In the Galápagos Darwin felt, with a deep inward stirring which he never forgot, that he had been brought very near to "that great fact—the mystery of mysteries—the first appearance of new beings on earth."

The words the young scientist used were guarded; they did not deny the separate creation of each kind of living being, though they subtly called it into question. And yet all of Darwin's actions and reasoning showed that the unconforming facts of the life of the islands had all but convinced him that one species is descended from another. In no other way could he have sensed so acutely the strain that the similarities and dissimilarities of the

Galápagos species placed on the doctrine of special creation. He had glimpsed a different explanation of life's
origins.

Darwin by this time fully understood the dangerous
implications of the thoughts running through his mind.
Among the little leather-backed pocketbooks which he
carried with him on all his trips, and in which he jotted
down his impressions of the moment, was one on orni-
thology. One day he entered the full details about the
differences in the birds of the various islands. The way
in which they had grown apart reminded him of the
differences he had seen in the wolf-like fox of the east
and west Falkland Islands. Perhaps the zoology of archi-
pelagos should be further investigated, for, Darwin set
down in his notebook, such facts "would undermine the
stability of species."

This revealing, significant statement lay hidden in the
unpublished pages of his ornithological notebook. Nowhere else did Darwin say in so many words that what
he had seen in the Galápagos and around the world
might "undermine the stability of species." He was too
keenly aware of how much he did not know, and of
how much was inexplicable in that great mystery of mysteries, to make any bold or even modest public claims. It
would take Charles Darwin more than a quarter of a
century to assemble the monumental evidence that he
felt was essential before he would dare to shock an in-
credulous world with the theory that species were not
fixed and final but had changed and evolved.

But on October 20, 1835, when the *Beagle* sailed
away from the craters of the Galápagos and turned her
head toward the South Seas, Charles Darwin had sensed
the great truth of evolution. The unique giant tortoises,

the aboriginal lizards that hunted under the sea for their food, and the peculiar little finches with their graduated beaks had given the twenty-six-year-old naturalist a probable answer to that most profound of all problems: how the life of this earth originated and developed.

Or, it should be said, the Galápagos and much that had gone before had given him an insight into that great mystery and a direction.

TWO

BEGINNINGS

ENGLAND was in the exhilarating throes of a new day when the two grandfathers of Charles Darwin first met. And they were distinctly men of that day, helping to shape it. The urge to strike out afresh, to move and to think in new terms, did not come into the Darwin line with Charles Darwin.

It was probably in 1760, though it may have been in 1761, that Dr. Erasmus Darwin, an unusually successful young physician, was called to treat a rising young potter named Josiah Wedgwood. Almost at once the two men—the two grandfathers of Charles Darwin —became friends. There was much to draw them together.

Dr. Darwin had been born in 1731. After completing his medical studies at Cambridge and Edinburgh, he had entered practice at Lichfield. Soon after his arrival in the central English town, he was consulted by a "young gentleman of family" whose illness had only grown worse under the ministrations of the other physicians of the district. By the use of a "novel method of treatment," Dr. Darwin effected the patient's speedy recovery. From that moment he was on his way to becoming not only the leading physician of Lichfield, but a doctor with a national and international reputation.

But the interests of the tall, heavy-set young physician with the full-bottomed wig that would not stay aright and the flow of heady talk, did not end with medicine.

His close friends, James Watt and Matthew Boulton,

were busy with the improvement and development of their new steam engine, which even then was beginning to remake the face of England. Dr. Darwin, one of the few who foresaw the mighty potentialities of the new device, once proposed to Boulton that they go into partnership to produce a steam locomotive that the doctor had conceived and planned to patent. The scheme did not work out, but the doctor put his soaring ideas into verse as he jogged about the countryside in the sulky he had designed with a skylight and full facilities for writing:

> Soon shall thy arm, Unconquer'd Steam!, afar
> Drag the slow barge, or drive the rapid car;
> Or on wide-waving wings, expanded bear
> The flying chariot through the fields of air.

Josiah Wedgwood, the patient Dr. Darwin was summoned thirty miles to visit, was one of the new industrialists, absorbed not only in putting the amazing new inventions to work, but in the new canals and roads they were requiring and in the political changes they were bringing.

Josiah Wedgwood had been born in 1730, seventeen months before the doctor. At the age of nine the death of his father had forced him to leave school and go to work in his brother's pottery. Working in the shop, which was only a room at the rear of the family's modest home, he thoroughly learned his trade. He later picked up some of the finer points in a partnership with Thomas Whieldon, one of the master potters of the day. As he learned the traditional ways of the potter with his clay, Josiah also was experimenting with new methods of his own. In 1759 he was ready to go into business for himself and to produce the unique and beautiful Wedgwood ware that in two hundred years has only gained in distinction and value. It was a success from the beginning.

Josiah was soon England's foremost potter, and his Etruria Works—a name suggested by Dr. Darwin—was a small but important cog in England's burgeoning world trade. A cream ware service presented to Queen Caroline brought him the title and position of Royal Potter, and an order from the Empress Catherine of Russia for a dinner service decorated with thirteen hundred English scenes confirmed the world-wide fame and pre-eminence of his ware.

All the while the Darwin-Wedgwood friendship flourished and deepened. Josiah Wedgwood frequently was a guest at the meetings of the Lunar Society—the Lunatics—a club of kindred spirits organized by the doctor. What rare occasions their dinners were—they were always held at the full of the moon in order that the members might be well lighted on their homeward way—was conveyed by the doctor when he was forced to miss a meeting: "Lord," he wrote, "what inventions, what wit, what rhetoric, metaphysical, mechanical and pyrotechnical will be on the wing, bandied like a shuttlecock from one to another of your troupe of philosophers! while I, poor I my myself I, imprisoned in a post-chaise, am joggled, jostled, and bumped, and bruised along the king's highroad to make war upon a stomach-ache or fever."

Both the doctor and the potter were Whigs, men of independent mind who were sympathetic to the ideals of the French Revolution and to the American struggle for independence. Both also abhorred slavery. The doctor once wrote: "Fierce SLAVERY stalks and slips the dogs of Hell." Josiah expressed his equally strong feelings by designing a cameo on which he depicted a black slave kneeling in chains. It bore the words: "Am I not a man and brother?"

As their success grew, both of these remarkable grand-fathers of Charles Darwin expanded their interests into related fields that brought them added renown. Josiah gave more time to the design of costly medallions and classical vases and became a noted antiquarian. The doctor, as his income increased—he refused to go to London to become Royal Physician to George III—gave increasing attention to his writing.

In 1794 he finished his *Zoonomia*, a major work to which he had given almost twenty years and which was designed not only to "unravel the theory of disease," but to explain life itself. With uncanny prescience he asked: "Would it be too bold to imagine that, in the great length of time since the earth began to exist, perhaps millions of ages before the commencement of the history of mankind—would it be too bold to imagine, that all warm-blooded animals have arisen from one living fila-ment . . . ?"

The question was no casual one. The doctor had been impressed by the classifications of plants and animals made by Linnaeus and Buffon. That all living things should fall into groups with strong family resemblances suggested to the doctor that one related group might have given rise to the other. It was an insight all the more remarkable because both the great Swedish and French classifiers had insisted, on the evidence of the same facts, that at least the elemental species had been created as they were and had never changed. No one, they had pointed out, had ever been able to transmute one species into another.

The doctor, in a half-poetic, half-intuitive way, dared
to speculate on how new species might have evolved.
In their "embryon state" all quadrupeds and mankind
were "aquatic animals." If it might be supposed that
certain "animalcules" had somehow made their way to
dry land and in response to the air and harsh conditions
had gradually acquired new powers in order to preserve
their existence, then, he argued, they might "by innumerable successive reproductions for some thousands, or
perhaps millions of ages . . . have produced many of
the vegetable and animal inhabitants which now people
the earth." Eight years before Lamarck published his
Recherches sur l'organisation des corps vivans, Lamarck's
first statement of his famous doctrine, Dr. Darwin said in
his *Zoonomia*: "All animals undergo perpetual trans-
formations which are, in part, produced by their own ex-
ertions, in consequence of their desires and aversions
. . . and many of these acquired forms are transmitted
to their posterity." It was Lamarck's famous theory of
the inheritance of acquired characteristics stated almost
in the words the French scientist was later to use.

Nevertheless, it seemed extremely difficult to explain
how "the same living filament" might have produced
animals as different as the cold-blooded fishes and the
warm-blooded mammals. And yet, the doctor asked,
were there not creatures such as the whales and seals and
the frog "which unite or partake of both of these orders
of animation?"

The doctor pointed too "to the great changes produced in various animals by artificial or accidental cul-
tivation." Some horses had been bred for swiftness and
some for speed; the hound and spaniel were fine ex-
amples of dogs developed for acuteness of smell; cattle

and sheep had undergone "so total a transformation that
we are now ignorant from what species of wild animal
they had their origin." Many years later the doctor's
grandson was to draw in the same way upon the same
evidence to build and confirm his own theory of the
origin of species.

Occasionally too the doctor liked to reason from
his own observations. He, well before his grandson,
could see the large significance of the small, seemingly
inconsequential action. He told of "one circumstance
that fell under my eye and shewed the power of reason
in a wasp." One day as he sat in his garden he noticed a
wasp that had killed a fly and was attempting to carry it
away. In the strong breeze that was blowing, it could
make no headway. It thereupon alighted, clipped off the
wings of the fly, and made off with its prize without
further difficulty. "Go, proud reasoner," said the doctor,
"and call the worm thy sister."

The idea that there might have been a progression of
life was, of course, an ancient one. Both the Greeks and
the Romans had sensed it, and had set it down in a
partly scientific and partly mythical way. During the
Middle Ages, however, the forms of living things were
declared the work of a higher power and an act of creation beyond human questioning. Not until the revival of
science in the eighteenth and nineteenth centuries did
men once more begin to ask if there might be some
other explanation of the close relationships they saw in
many of the living things about them. Dr. Darwin was
keenly aware of the dissatisfaction with the old omnipo-
tent explanation, and did not hesitate to explore the possibility of a new approach.

The *Zoonomia* created strong interest. It went into

three editions in seven years and was translated into French, Italian, and German. But on the whole it seems to have been valued more as a textbook on disease than as an explanation of life's origins. Actually, the doctor's speculations and crowded fancies were considered so far-fetched and loose that for a time the term "Darwinizing" was used to indict anything smacking of wild hypothesis.

As a boy, Charles Darwin read this famous book of his grandfather's, and he heard it discussed in his home, though his grandfather had died seven years before he was born. Darwin always felt that he had not been particularly influenced by the *Zoonomia*. When he re-read it after he had started on his own massive compilation of data on the origin of species, he was sorely disappointed. He felt, he said in his autobiography, that the proportion of speculation was too large for the facts.

This was, of course, a mature judgment of the *Zoonomia*'s obvious failure to produce the evidence for its grand conclusions. Darwin, with his reticence and his carefulness, was not one to attempt an appraisal of how a young boy's imagination may have been stirred by this bold effort of one man to understand the world around him, or by the fact that this man was his grandfather.[1] Even so, Darwin added in his autobiography: "It is probable that hearing rather early in life such views maintained and praised may have favoured my upholding them under a different form in my *Origin of Species*."

---

[1] Overt pride in family was anathema to the Darwins. Gwen Raverat, Charles Darwin's own granddaughter, explains in her charming book *Period Piece* that she and her cousins "always felt embarrassed if our grandfather were mentioned, just as we did if God were spoken of. . . . Of course it was very much to our credit to own such a grandfather; but one mustn't be proud or show off about it. . . ."

In the light of modern understanding of how deeply children are influenced by early impressions, this may well be a major understatement.

Dr. Erasmus Darwin had married soon after taking up his practice in Lichfield. His proposal, like everything else he did, was inimitably his own. To Mary Howard, an attractive, delicate girl of seventeen, he wrote: "Dear Polly: As I was turning over some mouldy old volumes, one I found after blowing the dust from it . . . to be a Receipt Book. . . . Upon one page was 'To Make Pye-Crust,' . . . then followed 'To Make a Good Wife.' 'Pshaw,' continued I, 'an acquaintance of mine, a young Lady of Lichfield, knows how to make this dish better than any other Person in the world. . . .'"

The doctor and his charmed Polly settled in an old half-timbered house, and there their three sons were born, Charles, Erasmus, and, in 1766, Robert Waring, who was to be the father of Charles Darwin.

The doctor's friend Josiah Wedgwood had married a little later, in 1764. He eventually became the father of three boys and three girls. At first, because of the ill-health of Mrs. Wedgwood, the children were sent away to school. When this later proved unsatisfactory, it was decided to educate them at home. The decision was influenced by Dr. Darwin, who strongly supported Josiah Wedgwood's preference for a "modern" over a classical education for both boys and girls. A young chemist who was also a scholar, and a Frenchman were engaged as tutors. Josiah actively supervised what at once became known as the Etruscan School.

For the 1770's it was a most unusual school. Lessons were short, the food was good, there were plenty of exercise and no corporal punishment. Young Robert Darwin was sent to share the lessons of his contemporaries John, Tom, young Josiah, and Susannah, and occasionally when there was illness at Etruria Hall school was held at the Darwin home. The Etruscans and the Darwinians, as they called themselves, were the warmest of friends. It was with great reluctance that Robert finally went north to Edinburgh to study medicine, and always any Etruscan on his way to London was expected to stop at Derby, where the doctor had moved after the death of his first wife and his second marriage.

The childhood friendship of Robert and Susannah slowly ripened into love and they were married in 1796. This marriage of the son and daughter of the two old friends fulfilled the hopes of both families and strengthened ties that otherwise might have weakened after the death of Josiah a year before. Susannah, like her two sisters, received a bequest of £25,000 from the large estate accumulated by her father. An even larger share went to two of the sons, and the Etruria Works to Josiah II.

Dr. Robert Darwin was a gifted physician. For half a century he was Shrewsbury's leading medical man, with a widespread practice and an income reputed to be as large as that of any doctor outside London.

Shrewsbury, where Dr. Darwin had chosen to enter practice, was an ancient town, built on a rocky hill around which the river Severn looped almost like a moat. There the early Britons had fought off the Romans, and later the English kings had used its river fastness to maintain their watch over the Welsh border. At the opening of the nineteenth century the medieval walls and the redstone castle at the river's neck still stood, crumbling but ever-present reminders of the past.

When Dr. Darwin and Susannah established their home there, Shrewsbury was a center of Midlands society. Each winter when the roads were bad the border aristocracy moved into town for a season of balls, suppers, hunts, and tea-drinkings. It was a last flowering, for in a few years better roads and the railroad were to make London accessible to the socially minded. But it was into this ordered, substantial, gay, and often snobbish society that Charles Darwin was born.

Charles—christened Charles Robert—was the fifth child of the doctor and Susannah. He came into the world on February 12, 1809, which may well be called a fateful day. It was on this same February 12, 1809 that the other man who along with Charles Darwin was most profoundly to influence their time, and perhaps the future, was born—Abraham Lincoln.

1809 might as justly be called a fateful year. Julian Huxley aptly named it an *annus mirabilis,* for it also brought the birth of Gladstone, Tennyson, Poe, Mendelssohn, Chopin, and Oliver Wendell Holmes.

Charles Darwin was born at The Mount, the big square Georgian house his father had built in 1800. It stood on the unfashionable side of Shrewsbury, but the doctor had deliberately chosen the site, a terraced bank above the Severn which commanded a beautiful unimpeded view of the river and of the rolling pastures and woods beyond. Gardens surrounded the house and stretched down to the river's edge.

• • •

Europe at the time of Charles's birth was in turmoil, engaged in a last desperate struggle with Napoleon. When Charles was six, in the soft lovely June of 1815, he heard the excited talk of the adults in the family. His parents and his Aunt Elizabeth, Mrs. Josiah Wedgwood II, who was visiting at The Mount, were acutely anxious. Tom Wedgwood, their seventeen-year-old nephew and Charles's cousin, was with the Scots Fusilier Guards at Waterloo.

And then there came rumors that Napoleon had surrendered. It seemed impossible to believe, and the whole household at The Mount waited with anxiety for the mail. As the coach clattered into the courtyard, family, children, servants dashed pell-mell to meet it. It was decorated with laurel and ribbons, and as this foretold, in Dr. Darwin's bag of mail was a *Courier* with the news "Buonaparte Has Abdicated."

"It is impossible to express our satisfaction and wonder," Elizabeth Wedgwood wrote to her sister. "Some of our abominable papers are strongly urging the putting of him [Napoleon] to death, but Dr. Darwin's scheme of sending him to St. Helena is the best that I have heard. . . . I take it for granted that we shall now have peace. The bells are ringing and the guns firing away at a great rate."

Elizabeth Wedgwood's assumption that there would be peace was essentially correct; a century of relative world peace did follow. Although it was far from complete, it brought freedom for the work that would be done by the six-year-old boy who shouted and jumped with excitement at the celebration hailing the downfall of Napoleon.

Two years later Charles's mother, Susannah, died.

Although Charles was eight then, he retained few recollections of her. Neither the stirring events of the day nor this personal tragedy left more that the most shadowy of conscious impressions. What did preoccupy the grave, gray-eyed little boy who sat for his portrait in a velvet suit with a white ruffled collar was his collecting. He had started to collect pebbles, coins, stamps, plants, and bird eggs—he would never take more than one of the latter from a nest. Later he preserved all the dead insects he could find, for after consulting his sister, he had decided that it was not right to kill live ones.

Not long after his mother's death Charles was sent as a boarding pupil to the Shrewsbury Grammar School, a school founded more than two hundred and fifty years earlier by Edward VI. The curriculum was strictly, rigidly classical, and was taught with a certainty that precluded any deviation for an unusual child.

The master, the Reverend Dr. Samuel Butler, informed parents: "While your son remains here he will always be exercised in Latin and Greek composition both in prose and verse and the higher he gets in school the more he will have of it."

For young Charles Darwin, who had no gift for either Latin or Greek in either prose or verse, that was a sentence of doom. As Charles struggled through his halting Latin verses, Dr. Butler would begin an ominous humming. Years later Charles could remember it with "fearful distinctness."

Charles's distinctive abilities were not of a kind to be appreciated either at school or at home. He was only ten when the family went to Plas Edwards, a Welsh seacoast resort, but no one was impressed that he knew enough about insects to point out that a large scarlet and black

Hemipterous insect and a *Cicid Cicindela* which he saw
there were not to be found in his own Shropshire. He
also read White's *Natural History of Selborne* and took
to watching birds and making notes on their habits. It
was such a fascinating business that he wondered why
every gentleman did not become an ornithologist.

Or perhaps a chemist. Erasmus, Charles's older
brother, had set up a chemical laboratory in a toolhouse
in the garden. With Charles assisting, he made all the
gases and compounds, often working until late at night.
News of this peculiar and suspect operation seeped out at
the school, and Charles was promptly nicknamed "Gas."
Dr. Butler took an early occasion to rebuke him publicly
for wasting his time on such useless doings and called his
non-conforming pupil a *"poco curante."* Charles, not
knowing what the words meant, took them as a fearful
reproach.

Another, more glorious possibility had opened up;
Samuel Galton, Charles's step-uncle, taught him to shoot.
The first time Charles shot a snipe his hands trembled
so violently with the wonderful excitement of it that he
could scarcely reload his gun. "I do not believe anyone
could have shown more zeal for the most holy cause than
I did for shooting birds," Darwin recalled many years
later.

Dr. Darwin tolerated such enthusiasms, though he
valued them little more than Dr. Butler, and he, like
the master, was a dominating figure whose opinions
could not be disregarded.

Dr. Darwin was six feet two inches tall and enor-
mously heavy; his weight was well over three hundred
and fifty pounds. His son, who did not make such statements lightly, said that he was the biggest man he ever

saw. When the doctor went into the not overly sturdy homes of some of his poorer patients, he often sent his coachman in ahead to test the stairs. He had strong views on nearly all subjects and liked to hold forth upon them at length. Before dinner at The Mount there was likely to be an hour or more of dissertation by the doctor. Elizabeth Wedgwood, Charles's young cousin, on a visit to The Mount wrote home: "We dined at half past one, drest afterward, and sat about three hours expecting the tide to come in about dark and rather still and awful the evening was." The tide, of course, was the doctor. Most guests found the atmosphere at The Mount more than a little formidable.

The doctor was, understandably enough, displeased at the way his son was getting on in school. "You care for nothing but shooting, dogs, and rat-catching," he once lectured his son, "you will be a disgrace to yourself and all your family."

The words cut deep; Charles never forgot them, but he explained in his autobiography: "My father, who was the kindest man I ever knew and whose memory I love with all my heart, must have been angry and somewhat unjust when he used such words." As he grew older and increasingly independent of his father, Charles's feeling for him deepened into an overawed, extreme reverence. It was so marked that it escaped no one.

Charles's own son, Sir Francis Darwin, was well aware of it: "It was astonishing how well [my father] remembered his father's opinions, so that he was able to quote some maxims or hint of his in most cases of illness." Charles's daughter Henrietta, Mrs. Richard Litchfield, was likewise impressed by it: "No son could have been more devoted or reverent than our father. Indeed, when he said 'My father thought or did so and so,' we all knew that in his mind there could be no further question in the matter; what his father did or thought was for him absolutely true, right, and wise."

For all of his Olympian bearing the doctor could be jovial and was a shrewd and perceptive judge of human behavior. He told his son that when ladies consulted him, complaining in a vague way of their health, he would suggest that they had been suffering in their mind. This generally opened the floodgates and they poured out their troubles with little more said about bodily aches. This, long before the days of Freud and psychosomatic medicine.

The influence of this huge, overbearing, and brilliant man on his extremely sensitive young son went to the core. There is every indication that what the doctor was exerted a determinative effect in making Charles Darwin the exceptional human being that he became. It is significant that, despite Charles Darwin's boundless, touching reverence for his father, he himself, when he grew older and particularly when he became the head of a family, was the exact opposite of his father. Where the doctor was dictatorial, Charles was gentle almost beyond compare; where the father advanced every opinion as fiat, Charles Darwin always begged the world and his own children in particular never to accept any statement of his unless they were convinced of its truth; where the doctor upbraided him, Darwin hardly ever uttered a reproving word to his children and on the few occasions when he did so spent a sleepless night; where the doctor was a man of overwhelming physical appearance and health, his son was slender and suffered almost constant ill-health; where the doctor was hearty, Charles was af-

fectionate and anxious; where Dr. Darwin unquestion-
ingly manipulated people to his own ends, his son could
not endure even the ordinary give and take of social life.

But all of this was below the surface. Charles Darwin
had no conscious thought except love and admiration for
his stern parent. An upbringing that has turned many
children into replica tyrants made him the kindest and
most considerate of men—and perhaps a lifelong semi-
invalid. In those deep emotional and psychological
abysses that Charles Darwin did not explore, the picture
of the doctor may have been a different one.[2]

Dr. Darwin had decided, if there had ever been any
doubt in his mind, that both his sons should follow him
and their grandfather into the practice of medicine.
Erasmus, the older brother of Charles, had begun his
medical studies at Cambridge, but in the fall of 1825
was to go to the University of Edinburgh. Because
Charles was "doing no good" at school, the Doctor held
that he should go too, though at sixteen he was young for
medical school.

The summer before they left, the doctor attempted
to give Charles a taste of what medicine might be by
sending him to attend some of his charity patients—in
those days no one was troubled by such a proceeding.
But even at sixteen it was impossible for Charles to be
anything but gentle in dealing with any other human

[2] Dr. Douglas Hubble, who has made a study of Charles
Darwin's ill-health, said in an article in the *Lancet*, British
medical publication, on December 26, 1953 that Darwin learned
at an early age to accept any painful emotion without an out-
ward aggressive reaction. "He had learnt by his contact with
an authoritarian and tyrannical father to discharge aggression
down his receptive and much-travelled autonomic pathways,
there to disturb his gastro-intestinal functions," said Dr. Hubble.

read widely and attended university gatherings at which
notable men of science spoke. In this way he heard
Audubon lecturing on the birds of North America and
was at the meeting of the Royal Medical Society at
which Sir Walter Scott presided. Charles listened with
"reverence and awe" as Sir Walter said that he did not
feel fitted for the honor bestowed upon him.

The summer and early fall between Darwin's two
school years at Edinburgh were a happy time. Charles
went to Paris with his Uncle Josiah Wedgwood to
bring home his cousins, Emma—later to be his wife—
and Fanny. In the fall there was Maer, beloved Maer,
the home of Uncle Jos, and the partridge-shooting.

Maer must have been one of the most pleasant of all
houses. The Wedgwoods, their cousins the Darwins,
the many other relatives who came not only for week-
ends but often for visits of months, and the friends who
came and went in a steady stream, all looked upon it as
the place above all others where life was free, gracious,
interesting, and lived as they felt in their hearts it should
be. In large part this was a reflection of Elizabeth Wedgwood, a woman whose loveliness has been captured for
all time in Romney's famous portrait of her and whose
warmheartedness was sung many times over in the letters of her husband, her children, her sisters, and her
friends.

The huge Elizabethan house sat on a slight rise above
the beautiful little lake that gave Maer its name. The
gardens, laid out by the famous designer Capability
Brown, stretched down to the lake and far out at either
side. Many of the spacious rooms were lined with books,
which were read and discussed, and Charles Darwin for
one never forgot the good talk, the music, and the "en-

chantment" of the summer nights on the portico with the sweet scent of the gardens drifting in on the breeze and with the house and woods reflected in the quiet surface of the lake.

Parties were always being given for the young; there were horses to ride, skating and boating on the lake, and the famous shooting in the autumn. The house was a joy to all who knew it.

Charles reluctantly left this haven to return to Edinburgh. By the end of his second year there, it was abundantly clear to everyone that he would never be a physician. From his father's standpoint, two more years had been wasted. Dr. Darwin's displeasure was not disguised; he could see his son turning into a dilettante collector or an "idle shooting man."

In this early third of the nineteenth century the only learned professions open to a gentleman were the law, medicine, and the ministry. As Charles showed no inclination for the law and would not follow him into medicine, the doctor decreed that he should become a clergyman. Charles, as ever respectful and acquiescent to his father, asked only for a little time to think over the decision. He concluded without much trouble that he could accept the creed of the Church of England and that he liked the idea of being a country clergyman, with the emphasis on the "country." This made it necessary for him to obtain a degree from one of the English universities.

The three years Charles spent at Cambridge, 1828–31, he always remembered as "the most joyful in my happy life." But he was remembering only the life he led there, the friendships he formed, and the books he read. His formal studies went little better than those at

Edinburgh or Shrewsbury. In the classics, for example, he did nothing except attend a few compulsory lectures, and they were very few. Before the examinations he brushed up enough with a tutor to pass with fairly respectable grades. Among the men at Christ College who did not go in for honors he stood tenth.

The Cambridge the nineteen-year-old loved had little to do with formal studies. As a young gentleman with a passion for hunting, shooting, and cross-country riding, he fell in immediately with the "sporting crowd." After a day in the saddle there would be a dinner with lusty drinking, "jolly singing," and playing at cards. Darwin felt in later years that he should regret this "dissipation," but the truth was that he looked back on these gatherings with much pleasure. "We were all in the highest spirits," he explained.

What he wholly put his heart into was beetle-collecting. "Bug-hunting" was then the fashion at the university, and Charles, a natural recruit, was introduced to it by his cousin William Darwin Fox. His zeal was practically unlimited.

One day while he was out beetle-hunting, Charles ripped some old bark from a log. There were two rare beetles. He had grabbed one in each hand at the very moment he spied a third, a new kind that he could not bear to lose. He acted fast. He popped the one in his right hand into his mouth and seized the third. Unfortunately for this scheme of capture, the beetle ejected a mouthful of intensely acrid fluid. Even Charles's ardor could not take it. He had to spit out his prize, and in the confusion dropped the third beetle that had caused all the trouble.

His ingenuity was more successful later. In the effort

to outdo his fellow collectors, Darwin invented two clever new methods of collecting. He employed a laborer to scrape the moss off old trees and to collect the accumulated rubbish from the bottom of the barges that brought reeds from the fens. It was a happy inspiration, which produced many rare species.

"No poet ever felt more delight at seeing his first poem published than I did in seeing in Stephens' *Illustrations of British Insects* the magic words, 'Captured by C. Darwin, Esq.,' " Darwin confessed.

One friendship that he made and two books that he read at Cambridge were to go far in determining Darwin's future career. The friend was the Reverend John Steven Henslow, professor of botany and a man with a genius "for drawing conclusions from long continued minute observations." Both loved long walks through the beautiful Cambridge countryside, and before his third year had ended, Darwin had become known as the "man who walks with Henslow."

The books were Alexander von Humboldt's *Personal Narrative of Travels to the Equinoctial Regions of America during the Years 1799–1804* and Sir John Herschel's *Introduction to the Study of Natural Philosophy.* After reading von Humboldt, Darwin felt that he had to travel and that in particular he had to see the wonders of Tenerife in the Canary Islands. He copied out long passages telling of the glories of this island and read them aloud to Henslow and any friends he could persuade to listen. He even went so far as to inquire about ship schedules. Herschel's book stirred in Darwin "a burning zeal to add even the most humble contribution to the noble structure of Natural Science."

As Darwin had entered Cambridge after Christmas,

he was required to remain in residence for two terms after passing his examinations in January 1831. Henslow persuaded him to use the time to begin the study of geology. That summer Professor Adam Sedgwick was planning a geological study of some of the older rocks of Wales, and Henslow persuaded him to permit Darwin to accompany him, which he gladly did. Before they set out, Sedgwick spent a night with the Darwins at Shrewsbury. Darwin could scarcely wait to tell him about a tropical shell that a worker had found in a gravel pit near The Mount. Sedgwick answered that if it really had been embedded there it would be a great misfortune to geology, for it would upset all that was known about the superficial deposits of the Midland counties.

The remark was a revelation to Darwin. "Nothing before ever made me realize," he said, "that science consists in grouping facts so that general laws and conclusions may be drawn from them."

The fledgling geologist enjoyed the expedition, but he hurried back over the shortest cross-country route he could lay out to reach Maer in time for the opening of the fall shooting, "for at that time I should have thought myself mad to give up the first days of partridge shooting for geology or any other science."

On his way to Maer Darwin stopped briefly at The Mount. A letter was waiting for him, a letter that was to change his life completely, and it came from Henslow. Captain Robert Fitzroy, of the Royal Navy, had asked Henslow to recommend a young man who would go without pay as a naturalist on H.M.S. *Beagle's* forthcoming voyage around the world.

Darwin was incoherent with delight. A two-year

voyage around the world—not only Tenerife, but Tierra del Fuego, the South Seas, and other places whose very names were fabulous to speak. And Henslow had said: "I think there was never a finer chance for a man of zeal and spirit . . . Don't put on any modest doubts or fears about your disqualifications. I think you are the very man they are in search of. . . ."

The vaulting elation of this magic moment did not last long. Dr. Darwin shattered it. He did not want another change of profession, and this was a wild scheme that would contribute nothing to the character of a clergyman. It was a dangerous, useless offer that others must have turned down. The doctor made only one concession. Charles was going to Maer. If he could find a single man who thought it a sensible idea, the doctor would give his consent.

Dr. Darwin had wrongly estimated the Wedgwoods. All of them thought it the finest, most exciting proposal they had ever heard of. What was more, Uncle Jos thought it so promising that he was willing to try to persuade the doctor to change his mind. Charles put down in writing his father's objections, all eight of them, and Uncle Jos drafted an answer, point by point. The pursuit of natural history should not be disreputable to a clergyman, but suitable for him; Charles would be as likely to acquire and strengthen habits of application as if he remained at home; if Charles were absorbed in professional studies the journey might not be advisable, but his pursuit of knowledge was on the same track he would follow on the expedition; and this was such an opportunity of seeing men and things as happens to only a few.

Charles added a note of his own, touching in its eagerness: "The danger appears to me and all the Wedgwoods not to be great. . . . The expense cannot be serious, and the time, I do not think anyhow, would be more thrown away than if I stayed at home. . . . I cannot think that it would unfit me thereafter for a steady life. . . . But pray do not consider that I am so bent on going that I would for one single moment hesitate if you thought that after a short period you should continue uncomfortable."

The letters were dispatched, but on second thought Uncle Jos decided that he and Charles should follow them personally. Dr. Darwin gave in; he graciously granted his consent and agreed to finance the voyage. Charles assured him that he would have to be "deuced clever" to spend more than his allowance on board the *Beagle*. At this the doctor commented: "They tell me you are deuced clever."

"Gloria in excelsis is the only moderate beginning I can think of," Darwin exulted, telling Henslow the wonderful news.

After some additional negotiations the matter was settled, and in due time Charles's formal orders came from the Admiralty.

Almost as though he could know, Darwin wrote to Captain Fitzroy: "What a glorious day the fourth of November will be for me. My second life will then commence, and it shall be a birthday for the rest of my life." [4]

And so it was.

[4] November 4th was then set as the sailing date.

THREE

THE VOYAGE OF THE *BEAGLE*—
Tenerife to Tierra Del

ON the 27th of December 1831 the good east wind
H.M.S. *Beagle* had been awaiting began to blow. Anchor was weighed, and the ten-gun brig tacked out
beyond the Devonport breakwater.

Captain Fitzroy, Second Lieutenant James Sulivan,
and Charles Darwin went ashore for a final luncheon, a
luncheon of mutton chops and champagne chosen as a
fitting farewell to an England they knew they were leaving for at least three years. They rejoined the *Beagle* at
two o'clock. The orders were given, every sail filled
with a light breeze, and the *Beagle* scudded out into the
gray winter sea on what was to be one of the great voyages of all time.

On board the one-hundred-foot, three-masted little
brig were seventy-two men: seven officers, five under-
officers, two surgeons, a purser, a squad of ten marines,
thirty-four seamen, six boys, two servants, three Fuegians
who were being returned to their homeland, a missionary,
and Charles Darwin, naturalist.

For this, her second scientific voyage, a voyage that
was to carry her around Cape Horn, across the South
Seas, round the Cape of Good Hope, and back to
England, the *Beagle* had been completely rebuilt, and
to make her more manageable in the tumultuous seas
in which she would sail, her deck had been raised and
her tonnage increased from 235 to 242 tons' burthen.
No expense or trouble had been spared in equipping her

for her specialized work of charting many of the world's still unknown waters and shores. Everything that could be was made of mahogany, Charles Darwin pointed out with pride in a pre-sailing letter to his family, and she carried an unusual set of twenty-four chronometers, all very good ones.

And she was to do her job well.[1]

But this voyage was to accomplish a far greater mission than the charting of unknown waters. It was to supply a new and world-upsetting answer to that most elemental of all unknowns: How did man and all the endless kinds of life around him originate?

This was to be the work of one man, the ship's twenty-two-year-old naturalist. In addition to his remarkably inquiring mind, his special equipment included a case of good strong pistols, an excellent rifle, a telescope, a geological compass, and his new microscope, about six inches long and four deep. A seamstress at The Mount had made him a dozen new shirts, and in the carpetbag in which his sister had sent some extra things shortly before the *Beagle* sailed were a pair of slippers, some lightish walking-shoes, and his Spanish books.

Another last-minute sailing gift, a book just published, was sent to him by Henslow. It was volume one of Charles Lyell's *Principles of Geology*. "Read it by all means," said Henslow, "for it is very interesting, but do not pay any attention to it except in regard to facts, for it is altogether wild as far as theory goes."

---

[1] The *Beagle* would return to England five years later with eighty-two coastal charts, eighty plans of harbors, and forty views, all for the Hydrographic Department of the Admiralty. A "view" probably was a silhouette of the coast as it looked from the sea.

Darwin's opportunity to read this peculiarly recommended book came soon. The *Beagle* was hardly beyond the breakwater when the breeze that filled her sails turned into an eight-knot-an-hour wind. The sea roughed up and Charles Darwin promptly became seasick. The only relief that he could get was to lie flat in his hammock, which was slung over the chart table that all but filled the tiny poop cabin allotted to Darwin and an officer. There was so little space that to make room for the foot clews of the hammock and for his long legs, Darwin had to remove the top drawer in the small bank of drawers in which he stored his clothes.

The sea grew even rougher with the aftermath of several storms, but Darwin found that as long as he stayed horizontal he could be sufficiently comfortable to use his eyes. At night he often lay watching the "moon and stars performing their small revolutions in their new apparent orbits." In the day as he read Lyell he felt that the history of the earth too was moving into a new orbit for him.

In 1832 most geologists still firmly believed that the earth had been shaped by the great flood of the Bible and other vast God-sent cataclysms. Lyell, a geologist who had just turned thirty-two when his book was published, was saying with revolutionary impact: "No causes whatever have from the earliest time to which we can look back, to the present, ever acted, but those now acting and they have never acted with different degrees of energy from which they now exert." He thus was maintaining that the winds, the rains, and the subterranean volcanic forces that were acting upon the earth from day to day were exactly the same forces that had altered it from the beginning of time and that had made its continents, its seas, its mountains, and its plains what they are.

This was the theory that Henslow considered "altogether wild." To Sedgwick also it was shocking and irreligious and a heresy that had to be fought. To Darwin, reading it as the *Beagle* plunged and shuddered through the Bay of Biscay, it was reason, it was light, and it was an exciting, fruitful theory that he could test and apply as the world unrolled before him.

On January 5th the *Beagle* sailed into spring. The air became mild and warm and the ocean smoothed down into a gently undulating plain. At daybreak on the sixth they came into sight of Tenerife, the island of Darwin's dreams. As the sun rose behind the famous Canary Islands peak, Darwin saw that it towered twice as high as he had imagined; fleecy clouds separated the snowy top from the rugged base, and the colors glowed rich and warm.

Just as the *Beagle* was about to drop anchor a boat came alongside bringing, as Darwin put it, "our death warrant." The cholera was raging in England—at Bilston hundreds had died, Emma Wedgwood had written to her aunt—and the *Beagle* party would not be allowed to land without observing a strict twelve-day quarantine.

"Oh misery, misery," Darwin wrote in his journal, "those who have never experienced it can never imagine what a gloom it cast on everyone."

The ship fell silent while Captain Fitzroy decided. Then he ordered: "Up jib," and she sailed away for Praia, in the Cape Verde archipelago, four hundred miles off the coast of French West Africa.

In the calm balmy days that followed, Darwin con-
soled himself as well as he could by collecting marine organisms. He devised a four-foot-long bunting bag that
he towed behind the *Beagle*. "The number of animals
the net collects is very great," he recorded, "& fully
explains the manner so many animals of large size live
so far from land. Many of these creatures are most exquisite in their forms & rich colours. It creates a feeling
of wonder that so much beauty should be apparently
created for so little purpose."

All his life Charles Darwin was to have trouble with
his sentences, but there never was any tangling in the
way his mind worked. He saw at once that the presence
of the little organisms made it possible for the big fish to
live far out in the ocean—an obvious conclusion but an
accurate observation.

On January 16th the *Beagle* reached São Tiago, in
the Cape Verde Islands, and Darwin for the first time
set foot in the tropics. He tried to make a calm analysis
of the geologic features of the dry, hilly island, but how
could anyone fresh from the sea and walking for the
first time in a grove of coconut trees think of anything
other than his own happiness! Charles feasted on oranges,
which he found selling for a shilling a hundred, and
tasted his first banana, which he did not like—"mawkish
and sweet and with little flavor."

When he could bring his thoughts around to "geolo-
gizing" and looked at the island with the eyes of Lyell,
he discovered a wonder even greater than the tropics.
Straight across the face of the seacliff that ran along the
harbor was a horizontal band of white about forty-five
feet above the water. Darwin climbed up to examine it
and found to his amazement that it was made up of

calcareous matter in which thousands of shells were embedded. What was even more astounding, nearly all of
them were exactly like the shells he gathered on the
beaches below. The white band was topped with a thick
layer of basalt.

If he reasoned according to Lyell's theory, Darwin
could reconstruct what had happened. The basalt must
have flowed into the ocean when the white shelly bed
was lying at the bottom of the water. He could trace the
changes produced in the shells by the tremendous heat;
in some places they had been converted into a crystalline
limestone and in others into a compact, spotted stone.
Then at some time in the past—probably at not too distant a time, as the shells were still of the same species as
the living shells—the island must have been gradually
upheaved and the shells moved into their position forty-
five feet above the sea.

By observing, by reasoning, by comparing, the changes
that had occurred could be mapped and the present
earth could be explained. It was an intoxicating, moving
thought. Tired and happy, Darwin stretched out on the
beach at the foot of the cliff. The sun beat warm upon
him, at his hand were some curious desert plants, and
just in front of him in a tidal pool grew brilliantly
colored corals—he remembered every detail, for this
was a notable moment. There for the first time the
thought came to him that he, Charles Darwin, could
write a book on the geology that he had just seen and
that he would see. A whole new prospect had opened,
and it made him "thrill with a delight" that no thought
of medicine or the ministry had ever aroused in him.

Leaving the islands, the *Beagle* sailed a straight course
for Brazil over a sea so calm Darwin happily argued that

it could not be the same element that had tossed them about so brutally in the Bay of Biscay. Lying on the deck in the sun, he read von Humboldt's lyric descriptions of the Brazilian forest. But when the *Beagle* had landed and Darwin walked for the first time into that majestic forest, he knew that no words could approach the actuality.

The lofty trees, the brilliant flowers and fruits, the strange parasitical plants, the fantastically colored birds and insects that flitted everywhere—before he could absorb the beauties and wonder of one, another drew his dazzled eyes. And over all this "sublime grandeur" lay a paradoxical mixture of silence and sound; in the inner recesses a universal silence seemed to reign, and yet a short distance away the noise of the insects beat upon the ears. At night, on the *Beagle* anchored several hundred yards from the shore, they heard the throbbing chorus. Darwin could only describe his mind as a "chaos of delight," and he knew then as he did many other times on the voyage that the beauty he was seeing would remain with him as a treasure to be cherished and enjoyed for all of his life.

Darwin returned to the forests many times while the *Beagle* made her Brazilian coastal surveys. As he set out from the town quarters that he sometimes established, fly net over his shoulder, clasp knife swinging on a string around his neck, and bulging with his pistols, compass, and other equipment, he always collected a queue of gawking and delighted men, women, and children. "I don't know whether they afforded me or I them the most amusement," Darwin laughed.

To please the children, he would pull some of his equipment from his capacious pockets—nets, snares,

bottles, pillboxes for the insects, string, the big handkerchiefs that he used for measuring and wrapping. The
children would sing out: "Sin, sin, full of sin," doubtless
thinking that all of this strange paraphernalia could only
belong to "*al diabolo.*"

As Darwin was walking one day in the forest he came
upon a curious fungus called *Hymenophallus*. He knew
the English phallus and knew that it attracted beetles by
its odious smell. As he walked along holding it in his
hand, a beetle alighted on it. Darwin stopped in surprise. There in Brazil and in distant England the same
type of relationship had developed between plants and
insects of the same families, though all belonged to different species. To see, to understand that the beetle's
flight was not by chance, was to face a basic question.
Why, if the Brazilian and English fungi had been separately created, had the same link developed between
them?

Darwin's collections—plants, rocks, animals, spiders
by the hundreds, fish, reptiles—were growing apace and
more than apace. At every opportunity he shipped boxes,
casks, and crates back to England; even so, the litter
overflowed the narrow decks of the *Beagle*. John Clem-
ents Wickham, the "glorious fellow" in charge of the
decks, would growl at his friend Darwin that his specimens were "damned beastly devilment," and that: "If I
were skipper, I would soon have you and all your
damned mess out of the place."

The crew held their young naturalist in affectionate
respect. At first the younger officers called him "sir" because he dined with the Captain, but he was soon nicknamed the "Philosopher" and this was shortened to
"Philos." Darwin once overheard the boatswain of the

Beagle showing another boatswain around the ship:
"That's our captain, that's our first lieutenant; and
[pointing to Darwin] that's our fly-catcher."

At midnight on April 1st, all the watch below was
called up in turn—carpenters to repair a non-existent
leak, midshipmen to reef a sail, and so on. All were
caught by the April Fool joke. With everybody on
deck, Sulivan cried out: "Darwin! Did you ever see a
grampus? Bear a hand, then." Throwing on his clothes,
Darwin ran out, all eagerness, only to be greeted by a
roar of laughter from the whole crew.

The *Beagle's* Brazilian surveys were not completed
until the 5th of July. On that morning her anchor was
tripped and with a gentle breeze she stood out into the
harbor of Rio de Janeiro. In harbor at the time were the
Warspite, a seventy-four-gun line-of-battle ship that had
fought valiantly at Trafalgar, and the *Samarang.* As the
Beagle sailed by, their crews manned the rigging and
gave her three cheers, and the band struck up "To
Glory You Steer." It was a proud, unforgettable moment
for the *Beagle* and all aboard her.

For the remainder of 1832 and all of 1833 the
Beagle worked her way up and down the eastern coast
of South America. It was a raw land then, more unknown than known. Captain Fitzroy found that an
earlier calculation of the latitude of Rio de Janeiro was
off by four miles, and the *Beagle* frequently came upon
passages and islands that had never appeared on standard
maps.

It was, too, a land full of dangers. On one side trip of
the *Beagle* on which Darwin did not go, three of the
crew caught a fever from which they died. Often while
the ship was busy with her surveying, Darwin went on

long inland expeditions. On one excursion at Maldonado, on the eastern coast of Uruguay, he was amused
at the quantity of sabers and pistols with which his es-
corts armed themselves. They had not gone very far
along the road, however, before they heard that a
traveler who had taken that way the day before had just
been found with his throat cut. The dangers were not
imaginary.

There also were the inevitable hardships of explora-
tion. A large party from the *Beagle* went ashore in the
ship's four whaleboats to work at a "land mark." Darwin
went along to geologize. Before two of the boats were
ready to return, the surf rose and they found themselves
marooned on a beach with no food and only thin clothing. By huddling together they managed fairly well
until the rain began; then, Darwin recalled, "we were
sufficiently miserable." The next day an even heavier
surf roared up on the beach. The group breakfasted on
"two large birds & two gulls, & a large hawk that was
found dead on the beach." Dinner consisted of fish left
by the tide. By evening the Captain was able to send a
boat in close enough to toss over a cask of provisions,
which some of the men swam out and secured. But another night had to be spent on the beach, a night so cold
that there was snow on the Sierra de Ventana. "I never
knew how painful cold could be," said Darwin. "I was
unable to sleep for even a minute from my body shiver-
ing so much."

There were unforgettably amusing moments too, especially on the inland trips into country where visitors
seldom penetrated. At every house at which Darwin
stopped on another Maldonado excursion he was asked
to show the "powers" of his pocket compass. That a

stranger should know the road—direction and road were synonymous in this open country—excited unbounded astonishment. Darwin was asked whether the earth or sun moved, whether it was hotter or colder to the north, and where Spain was. He was frequently begged too to give an exhibition with the "prometheans" that he carried in his pocket and ignited by biting between his teeth. His habit of washing his face in the morning caused so much speculation that he was often cross-questioned about the singular practice.

At one huge *estancia*—it was ten leagues square—Darwin as a man of science was requested to answer one question and to answer it with all the truth of which he was capable. He trembled to think how deeply scientific it would be. It was: "Are the ladies of Buenos Aires not the handsomest in the world?" With the tact and skill of a diplomat, Darwin replied without hesitation: "Charmingly so." Delighted, his questioner begged for permission to ask one more question: "Do ladies in any other parts of the world wear such large combs?" Darwin assured him that they did not, and with the gratitude of a relieved mind his host exclaimed: "Look there, there's a man who has seen half the world and he says it is the case; we always thought so, but now we know it."

The country changed markedly as the *Beagle* pushed on southward. Closely allied plants and animals replaced one another, and Darwin saw that in ages past they also must have slowly and gradually moved to the south.

Beyond the Salado River, a little south of Buenos Aires, the coarse herbage of the pampas gave way to a

"carpet of fine green verdure." At first Darwin thought
that the change must have been due to some variation in
the soil. He was assured by the inhabitants that this was
not true; it was the grazing and manuring of the cattle
that accounted for the green cover.

Darwin asked himself if the appearance of the new
grasses was "owing to the introduction of new species,
to the altered growth of the same, or to a difference in
their proportional numbers?" He was not enough of a
botanist to be sure, but he suspected that many new species had been brought in by the cattle. It looked as
though the lines of richly manured land had served as
"channels of communication across wide districts."

In this area and in the Banda Oriental, farther to the
south, two European plants brought in by the early settlers, the cardoon and the giant thistle, had taken over
hundreds of square miles. The cardoon, a relative of the
artichoke, grew as high as a horse's back and the thistle
often as high as the crown of a rider's head. Their im-
penetrable mass had not only made the country impassable to man or beast, but had choked out the "aboriginal" grasses. It was the most dramatic example Darwin
had seen of new plants vanquishing the old. The young
naturalist was beginning to grasp the significance of the
struggle going on in nature. A change, the coming of
the cardoon and thistle, had altered the balance. The old
had succumbed; the new had won out in the never
ending struggle for living-space.

And this struggle had been going on for ages untold.
In the red mud that capped a gravel plain at San Julian,
in southern Argentina, Darwin found half the skeleton
of a remarkable extinct animal. It had the unmistakable
build of the rhinoceros, but the long tapering neck of the

llama or guanaco. It undoubtedly was an ancient ancestor of the llama, whose friendly attention Darwin had
found he could attract by lying on his back and kick-
ing his heels in the air.

Darwin wondered if Buffon, the French authority,
had he known of the lost gigantic species and of their
smaller, different descendants, would not have said that
the Creative Force had lost some of its power. If such an
argument were advanced, Charles saw at once there
would be one major difficulty: the creative force had not
diminished in all cases. Sea shells that lay buried with
the giant extinct quadrupeds were exactly like the sea
shells living on the beaches now; they were no larger.
There had been no loss, therefore, in creative power as
it applied to the shells, Darwin said in his notebooks.

What had exterminated so many species and even
whole genera? Darwin dismissed the idea of the great
catastrophe in which so many believed. He himself had
found fossil animals the entire length of South America,
and others had discovered them as far north as Bering
Strait. Any moment cataclysmic enough to have destroyed animals over such a vast territory surely would
have shaken the framework of the entire globe. Further-
more Darwin's own observations, as well as Lyell's arguments, had convinced him that the rise and fall of the
land and the changes it had undergone had been infinitely slow.

Surely no fact in the long history of the world is so
"startling as the wide and repeated extermination of its
inhabitants," he wrote. But if the problem were considered from a different point of view, it might not be
impossibly perplexing. Darwin could faintly perceive
both what the explanation might be and why the world,

in its "profound ignorance of the conditions of existence
of most animals," might have missed it.

All species had a tendency to increase geometrically;
some laid thousands of eggs, and even the slow breeders
soon would overrun the earth if they multiplied unchecked. That a check did intervene was evident. Even
invaders as successful as the prickly cardoon eventually
came to a halt and the established species, whether of
beetles or dogs or grasses, remained fairly constant in
numbers. Yet even the closest observer seldom was able
to tell when a check was applied or exactly what it was.

One fact, though, stood out clearly in this great veiled
maze through which Darwin was groping his way. Species first became rare and then extinct: that he could see
and demonstrate. In some of the older and deeper geological strata he often found vast numbers of certain
shells. In a strata above he would see that the same shell
had become rare. Then in still higher strata it would disappear altogether.

The same process was operating in the present. On
the Falkland Islands was a wolf-like fox so tame that
it would approach to take a piece of meat out of a
gaucho's hand. At the time of Darwin's visit, it had vir-
tually vanished from the eastern half of the islands and
was becoming rare in the western section. As its like
was to be found nowhere else in the world, Darwin did
not doubt that it was rapidly going the way of the dodo
and other rare species which had disappeared from the
face of the earth during the memory of man.

If it were conceded that rarity precedes extinction,
why then should there be surprise at extinction? "It appears to me," Darwin reasoned in his journal, "much the
same as to admit that sickness in the individual is the

prelude to death—to feel no surprise at sickness—but when the sick man dies to wonder, and to believe that he died through violence."

Other fossil finds opened other challenging questions. By swinging his pickax, Darwin uncovered teeth of mastodon, toxodon, and horse. To find a tooth of an ancient horse in South America was so surprising that Darwin took scrupulous care to make certain it had been embedded contemporaneously with the other fossil remains. He well knew that there was good evidence that no horse was living in the Americas at the time Columbus arrived.

"Certainly it is a marvellous fact in the history of Mammalia," he wrote, "that in South America a native horse should have lived and disappeared, to be succeeded in after ages by countless herds descended from the few introduced by the Spanish colonists."

A still more marvelous fact hinged upon the stained, decayed fossil teeth. Similar fossil teeth had been found in North America, a fact that could only mean, Darwin saw, that in the distant past the same species of animals had once lived in the northern and southern hemispheres. The same species of horse, mastodon, and elephant must once have roamed the prehistoric jungles and plains of both. Only later, then, had each hemisphere acquired the distinctive animals that it had always possessed within the history of man: North America its own gnawers, its ox, its sheep, its goat, antelope, and hollow-horned ruminants; and South America its peculiar gnawers, monkeys, llamas, peccary, tapir, opossums, sloths, anteaters, and armadillos.

With his growing knowledge of geology, Darwin was not afraid to speculate that the split had begun when the rise of the Mexican plateau and the submergence of some of the lands of the West Indian archipelago had cut off all travel of animals from the north to the south. With separation, different species had developed—this was the implication of the bold ideas jotted down by this young Englishman who had just passed his twenty-fourth birthday.

And where there was not one kind of wonder, there was another to stir Charles Darwin to his sensitive depths. A little south of the Plata they sailed on one very dark night into a sea glowing with a pale luminous light. The *Beagle* drove before her bows "two billows of liquid phosphorus and in her wake she was followed by a milky train." As far as the eye could reach the crest of every wave was bright and "from the reflected glare of these vivid flames" the sky above the horizon was "not so utterly obscure as over the vault of the heavens."

As he stood on the deck watching the play of this eerily beautiful light that was not of man's kindling, Darwin thought of Milton's description of the regions of chaos and anarchy. It was a display to give any man a sense of unease and disquiet. But, entranced as he was, Darwin could not forget that he was a naturalist. He hauled up a bucket of the glowing water, poured out a tumblerful, and stirred it vigorously. The sparks flew—arching, glowing flecks of light in the darkness. The tiny phosphorescent organisms that turned the water into flame passed through fine gauze, yet many were distinctly visible to the naked eye. Twelve hours later a net which Darwin had dipped into the water that night still sparkled as brightly as when it was first taken out of the water. Even the water in which he placed a jelly-fish became luminous. Darwin felt certain that when the

waves thus scintillated with green sparks and the blazing, glittering spectacle of light spread across the night
sea, it was "generally owing to minute crustacea."

After visits to Patagonia and the Falkland Islands,
just off the coast of southern Argentina, the *Beagle*
sailed on to Tierra del Fuego, that storm-lashed, gloomy
land at the very tip of the continent. They entered the
notoriously turbulent Le Maire Strait on one of the rare
days when wind and tide were running together, and
came safely to anchor in Good Success Bay, that first
stopping-place of Captain Cook. A group of savage
Fuegians followed the ship in, occasionally coming into
view in the dense forest that stretched down to the water's
edge. That night their wild cries could be heard aboard
the *Beagle*. In the morning Captain Fitzroy sent Darwin and a party from the crew ashore to communicate
with them.

"It was the most curious and interesting spectacle I
ever beheld," Darwin wrote. "I could not believe how
wide was the difference between savage and civilized
man."

The Fuegians were naked; the guanaco skins tossed
over their shoulders left "their persons as often exposed
as covered." The old chief, standing six foot three, wore
a fillet of white feathers tied around his tangled black
hair. Across his face ran two broad transverse bars: one,
bright red, stretching from ear to ear, covered the upper
lip; the other, chalk white, covered all the skin around
the eyes and even the eyelids. The *Beagle* party gave
him some red cloth, which he immediately tied around
his neck.

On the first voyage of the *Beagle* to Tierra del Fuego,
Captain Fitzroy had seized three Fuegians as hostages

for a boat that had been stolen. He had taken them and a boy he purchased for a pearl button back to England to be "instructed in religion." One of the group had died of smallpox, but an important object of the Captain on the second voyage was to return the others to their homeland.

York Minster, Fuegia Basket, and Jemmy Button, whose name identifies him, came back greatly changed by their exposure to civilization. Jemmy, a favorite of the ship, would come around to see Darwin when he was seasick and say in a plaintive voice: "Poor, poor fellow." He was fond of his kid gloves and highly polished boots. The three soon were landed, with a good store of equipment, among their undemonstrative relatives. Many months later when the *Beagle* again put in at Jemmy's home cove, all his finery and all his possessions were gone; he was back in a guanaco skin. But he had a young wife, and he refused an offer to take him to England again.

Hard days also lay ahead for the missionary whom the *Beagle* had brought to Tierra del Fuego. For life in this bleak, rugged land, missionary societies had showered him with wineglasses, butter-bolts, tea trays, soup tureens, mahogany dressing-cases, fine linens, beaver hats, and a variety of similar appurtenances of life in English society. After watching this assortment unloaded in the crude shack that the *Beagle* party built for him, Darwin indignantly wrote in his journal that night: "The choice of articles showed the most culpable folly & neglect." Most of the array soon was stolen, and to protect the missionary's life—the Fuegians were believed to be cannibals—the *Beagle* returned him to England.

Christmas Day, 1832 dawned fair enough for this

land of gales. While the crew celebrated on board, Darwin and Sulivan went ashore to climb the lofty peak near which the *Beagle* lay at anchor. When they came upon a large cave, they amused themselves by shouting and firing their guns to test its echoes. Then, falling into the spirit of the day, Sulivan began to roll huge stones down a precipice, and Darwin accompanied this crashing symphony by pounding on the rocks with his geological hammer. Only later did they learn that the "savage" Fuegians had been watching this strange performance.

That night the sky looked ominous and a great gale began to blow. So fierce was its fury, spray from the pounding waves drove over a cliff two hundred feet high. Only after six days did the storm let up enough for the *Beagle* to put out to sea. There, as she attempted to make her way westward, a succession of gales struck her. By the 13th the horizon was so narrowly limited by the wind-driven sheets of spray that they did not know exactly where they were, and the fearsome order was shouted constantly: "Keep a good lookout to leeward." At noon a tremendous sea broke over the lurching ship and wrenched away one of her "beautiful whale boats." The "poor *Beagle*" trembled at the shock and for a few dread moments would not obey her helm. Had another sea followed the first, Darwin said, "our fate would have been decided soon and forever." But the stanch *Beagle*, under the superb seamanship of Captain Fitzroy, righted herself and came up to the wind again. Lesser storms had sent many another ship to the bottom of these raging waters.

Exhausted by the twenty-four-day ordeal, the *Beagle* finally made a quiet anchorage. And there another party of Fuegians came down to meet her. They did not have even guanaco skins for protection, and one woman nursing a newborn child stood for hours gazing at the ship "whilst the sleet fell and thawed on her naked bosom and the skin of her naked baby."

Darwin thought long and often about this strange, isolated people and their forbidding land: "Whilst beholding these savages, one asks from whence have they come? What could have tempted a tribe of men to travel down the Cordillera or the backbone of America . . . to one of the most inhospitable countries within the limits of the globe? Although such reflections may at first seize the mind, yet we may feel sure they are partly erroneous. There is no reason to believe the Fuegians decrease in number. . . . Nature has fitted the Fuegian to the climate and the productions of his miserable country."

FOUR

THE VOYAGE OF THE *BEAGLE*—
the Andes and Atolls

IT was in June 1834, in the depths of winter, that the *Beagle* at long last sailed into the desolate Strait of Magellan and headed for the Pacific.

After her visit to Tierra del Fuego another year had been spent on the east-coast survey. Consequently, the season was at its most ominous when the *Beagle* entered Magdalen Channel, a recently discovered and seldom traveled passage between the strait and the sea. Dark, ragged clouds driving over the mountains all but obscured their jagged peaks and snowy cones, and the passage as well. By nightfall, nevertheless, the *Beagle* had reached Cape Turn, close by Mount Sarmiento, the second-highest peak at this end of the continent—only Mount Darwin, which Captain Fitzroy had named for his naturalist, towered higher. In the morning fortunately the clouds had lifted and the men aboard the *Beagle* saw Sarmiento's "sublime masses" of snow and the winding cataracts of beryl-blue ice that descended like jeweled chains to the sea.

It was a magnificent spectacle, though still not enough to make a man relish that part of the world, Darwin wrote to his sister. There was no comfort to be found anywhere at this end of the continent. The water was so deep they were unable to obtain an anchorage, and during a pitch-dark night of fourteen hours the *Beagle* was forced to stand off in the narrow channel. Once she came very near to the rocks.

Ahead lay numberless rocks and islets, on which the long swell of the open Pacific broke with an incessant and deafening roar. It was enough, Darwin noted, to make a landsman dream for a week about death, peril, and shipwreck. As they entered the Pacific through this formidable door, northerly gales swept down upon them. The *Beagle* rode them out with close-reefed topsail, fore trysail, and staysail, but even after the wind had ceased the great sea prevented their making any headway. In the midst of the tumult, death came to the *Beagle's* purser, who had long been sinking under a complication of disorders. A solemn funeral service was read on the quarter-deck and his body was lowered into the sea. Darwin, already desperately seasick, listened with the deepest gloom and sorrow to that "aweful and solemn sound, the splash of waters over the body of an old ship-mate."

But tragedy and storm were now over. In July they were at Valparaiso, Chile, where the climate "felt quite delicious," the sky was "so clear & blue, the air so dry, & the sun so bright." Added to these boons there were good fresh beef to eat, and an old school friend, Richard Corfield, who invited Darwin to stay in his very comfortable house.

Long-delayed letters from home also were waiting. During the voyage Darwin had been troubled by the fact that the one letter he had received from Henslow had not mentioned the many cases and crates of specimens he had shipped to Cambridge. Perhaps his collections were so poor that Henslow could not bring himself to say anything about them. Actually, Henslow was enthusiastic; in a letter that had been eighteen months on the way, he called Darwin's specimens splendid and invaluable to science. Charles was elated.

All the news from Shrewsbury was good too. Dr. Darwin had liked the section of the journal that his son had sent home, and even had warmly approved his hiring a servant. Almost from the beginning of the voyage Darwin had been badly in need of someone to assist him, both on shipboard and ashore. It was a rule of the ship that no one should leave it by himself "except in civilized ports." Although Captain Fitzroy had made a habit of assigning a man to Darwin, it took a crew member from other duties, and Darwin did not think this fair to the Captain. On the assumption that his father would consent, Darwin had hired a man and had found him indispensable. In addition to personal service he had learned to skin birds and prepare specimens, and on expeditions was a good man with a gun. Darwin, nevertheless, felt greatly relieved that his father did not object to his "extravagance."

Just beyond Valparaiso loomed the Andes, that omnipresent, divisive backbone of the continent toward which Darwin had looked for so long from the Atlantic coast and from the south. In August snow had closed all the mountains except the "basal parts." A crossing was impossible at that season, but Darwin set out with a guide and a string of mules for the lower slopes.

They made a camp on a height looking down on the bay of Valparaiso. As the sun set and the deep black shadows of the night enveloped the valleys below, the snowy peaks above them still caught the sun's last rays and turned a glowing ruby-red. Not until this "glorious sunset" had faded did they light a fire in their little arbor of bamboo trees and fry their *charqui*—slips of dried beef. Sipping his *maté* and listening to the occa-sional cry of the goatsucker and the shrill of the moun-tain bizcacha, almost the only sounds that broke the stillness, Darwin reveled again as he often had on the pampas in "the inexpressible charm of living in the open air."

Darwin made several trips to the gold and copper mines of the region. In his journal he factually reported what he saw, but behind his straight-marching words can be felt his sense of shock. In some of the mines the men still—"in the present day"—were removing water from the mine by carrying it up the shaft in leathern bags! The miners began work at dawn and did not quit until dark; for this they were paid one pound sterling a month and given three meals: a breakfast of sixteen figs and two loaves of bread, a dinner of boiled beans, and a sup-per of broken roasted wheat grain. They scarcely knew the taste of meat.

On one of these trips Darwin drank some *"chichi,"* a weak, sour Chilean wine, which he said "half poisoned me." Although he remained at the mine for several days until he felt better, his stomach again became upset when he began the long ride back to Valparaiso. One night he considered himself extremely lucky to find some clean straw for a bed—a success that later amused him with the relativity of all things. He laughed to think what he would have said to a bed of straw and "stinking horse cloths" if he had been in England and unwell.

When he finally reached Corfield's house he was seriously ill for more than a month. The ship's doctor prescribed "a lot of calomel and rest," and it seemed to work. Later Darwin sometimes felt that this sickness

may have been a factor in his lifelong ill-health, but at
the time he was principally concerned about the "griev-
ous loss of time" and the loss of the animals he had
hoped to collect.

As soon as Darwin was able to travel, the *Beagle*
left for a curtailed survey of southern Chile, and of the
island of Chiloé and the Chonos Archipelago, which lay
just off the Chilean coast. For a while, as Darwin lay
ill, the voyage itself had been endangered. Captain Fitzroy, angered at the Admiralty's order to sell the *Adven-
ture*, a tender he had bought to assist in the *Beagle's*
work, threatened to resign. Only strong argument from
the officers persuaded him instead to curtail the work he
thought should be done and to carry out the original
plan for a return through the Pacific. Darwin had felt
that the voyage was dragging out interminably and was
longing for England, but he was glad nonetheless to
know that he would not have to give up his "geological
castles in the air" or his hopes of seeing the South Pacific.

One day as Charles was wandering in the Chiloé
woods, he stretched out on the ground for a little rest and
felt the ground rock under him. The motion almost
made him giddy, it was so like that of a vessel in a cross-
ripple. The swaying motion that jarred him so lightly
was the famous earthquake of February 20, 1835, one
of the most severe in the region's long history of quakes.
Hardly a house was left standing in the town of Concepción, and gaping rents traversed the ground. Even
greater damage had been done by a huge tidal wave
that swept across the sea. As it broke at the head of the
bay, it tore loose a four-ton cannon and tossed it and a
schooner ashore as though they had been the lightest
pieces of driftwood.

For almost three years Darwin had been studying the elevation and subsidence of the land around the coast of South America. Here, almost before his eyes, the actual process was happening. By careful measurement he established that the big quake had raised the land around Concepción Bay between two and three feet, and on an island about thirty miles away Captain Fitzroy found putrid mussels adhering to rocks ten feet above the high-water mark. The inhabitants formerly had dived at low spring tide for these very shells. Darwin could understand with new clarity why he had found sea shells scattered over the land of the region at heights of as much as thirteen hundred feet above the water.

"It is hardly possible to doubt," he recorded in his journal, "that this great elevation has been effected by successive small uprisings, such as that which accompanied the earthquake of this year, and likewise by an insensibly slow rise which is certainly in progress on some parts of this coast."

Along the *Beagle's* route Darwin had received and eagerly read the second and third volumes of Lyell's geology. He had not only found Lyell right in his theory that the earth had been shaped by forces similar to those acting in his time, but in a letter to a cousin added: "I am tempted to carry parts to a greater extent even than he does." To see was to be convinced.

The mighty climax to which these workings of nature could rise lay ahead—the Andes. Darwin returned to Chile to make his long-anticipated crossing of the great walled mountains. For the journey he hired his guide of the earlier expedition and an *arriero* with ten mules and a *madrina*. The *madrina*, a little mare with a tinkling bell around her neck, acted, as Darwin explained it, as a "sort of stepmother to the mules"; they would follow her and her bell anywhere. Six of the mules were for riding; the others were loaded with supplies and extra food in case the snow should start to fall, for it was then March and already growing late for passing the Portillo, a high pass just east of Santiago.

Traveling was "delightfully independent." In the inhabited sections at night they would buy a little firewood, rent a pasture for the animals, and bivouac in a corner. Supper was cooked in a big iron pot, and under a cloudless sky all was right with the world.

They soon had to cross some of the mountain torrents that rushed down boulder-strewn courses with a roar like that of the sea. On the other side of the Andes, Darwin often had studied the vast plains of sand, shingle, and mud, and had questioned if he could be right in thinking that the rivers had deposited such immeasurable masses. But listening at night to the thunder of the Andes torrents and remembering that they had been running while whole races of animals disappeared from the earth, he could understand where the material of the plains had come from. He could understand how even mountains as immense as these could be worn down and their boundless substance be swept down to the plains, where he had seen it spread out, smooth, graded, and deep over miles without end.

They climbed higher and higher until the well-marked road turned into a zigzag track near the top of the Peuquenes range, which is the main western ridge of the Cordillera. At twelve thousand feet there was a transparency of the air, a confusion of distances, that gave one a sense of another world. The mules would halt every fifty yards, and the breath came lightly. The

Chilenos called this difficulty in breathing the *puna*—
"All the waters up here have *puna*," they would say;
or "Where there is snow there is *puna*." Darwin experienced a slight tightness across the head and chest, but
suddenly at about thirteen thousand feet he saw a strata
of shells. The *puna* was forgotten.

Shells at thirteen thousand feet, shells which must
once have lain in the matrix that still held them at the
very bottom of the sea! Darwin could identify many of
them: *Gryphæa, Ostrea, Turratella,* ammonites, and
small bivalves. He collected as many as time allowed.
If the ever present danger of snow had not made further
delay inadvisable, he would have "reaped a grand har-
vest."

Startling as it was to discover shells near the crest of
one of the world's highest mountain ranges, Darwin was
not unprepared for the find. As he climbed he had seen
with increasing astonishment that the upper reaches of
these towering mountains were made up of layer after
layer of sedimentary rocks, rocks that had been formed
in the sea by the unending downward drift of the skele-
tons and shells of living water organisms and the sedi-
ments of the earth. The upper parts of the Andes were
not, as science then thought, the once-molten outpour-
ing of a volcano or of a series of volcanoes.

Darwin knew that such findings would sound incredible to older geologists. In writing to Henslow he
cautiously began: "I know some of the facts, of the
truth of which I in my own mind feel fully convinced,
will appear to you quite absurd and incredible," and
then he told him of his discovery of the ocean-bottom
origin of the peaks of the Peuquenes and of their up-
lifting.

At the crest Darwin paused to look back at the glorious view. The sky was an intense blue; the profound valleys, the wild broken forms, the heaps of ruins piled up during uncounted ages, the bright-colored rocks contrasting with the mountains of snow produced a scene that Darwin felt no one could have imagined. Nothing moved except a few condors wheeling around the higher pinnacles. "I felt glad that I was alone," Darwin wrote. "It was like watching a thunderstorm or hearing in full orchestra a chorus of the Messiah."

Pushing on, they descended into the high mountainous country that lay between the Peuquenes and the Portillo chain, the other main ridge of the Andes. At the eleven-thousand-foot elevation where they camped, the miserable little fire that was all they could coax from a few scrubby roots did not begin to offset the piercing cold of the wind. Nor would it boil potatoes; after several hours they were as hard as ever, and even after they had remained on the fire all night they were uncooked. The next morning, following a potatoless breakfast, Darwin heard his two men talking about what had caused the trouble—"that cursed pot [a new one] did not choose to boil the potatoes."

There was another climb over the still higher though, Darwin was convinced, younger Portillo range. At its fourteen-thousand-foot crest the air was so clear and dry that the moon and stars took on a brilliancy Darwin had never seen matched. Electricity crackled at the least touch. When Darwin chanced to rub his waistcoat in the dark, it glowed as though it had been washed with phosphorus.

The descent to the Argentine pampas was short and steep, for on the Atlantic side the mountains rose abruptly from the plain. For a while a level, gleamingly white sea of clouds blocked out the view below, but once they were through this horizontal screen, the great Argentine plain stretched out below them as Darwin had long wanted to see it, from the west. And at first he was disappointed; it was like looking out across the sea. Then he made out some small irregularities to the north, and in the rising sun the rivers began to glitter like silver threads until they were lost in the immensity of distance.

Darwin swung a little northward in order to recross the Andes through the Uspallata Pass. The mountains there, a continuation of the grand eastern chain, were as amazing as those to the south. Darwin soon found that they were made up of alternating layers of lava and sedimentary rocks.

During his first two days of studying the formations and chipping off specimens, Darwin said to himself fifty times over that they looked exactly like the sandstone-lava formations he had seen in Patagonia and Chiloé. No shells, of course, would be found in such sandstone, but in the similar formations he had often come upon small pieces of silicified wood. Could there be such wood in these formations too? Almost without meaning to, he began what he was sure would be a "forlorn hunt."

He had gone only a short distance when at an elevation of seven thousand feet he saw some snow-white projecting columns standing alone in a little group on a bare mountain slope. Darwin hurried over to them. To his amazement and delight they proved to be petrified trees! Eleven were silicified and between thirty and forty had been crystallized into white spar. The stumps measured from three to five feet in circumference.

It was not difficult for Darwin to interpret the "marvellous story this scene unfolded," though he continued to feel that he scarcely dared to believe such perfect evidence.

Once upon a time the stone stumps had stood green and budding on the shores of the Atlantic. The ocean, which in the 1830's was more than seven hundred miles distant, had then rolled up to the very foot of the Andes. As had happened many times before, this shore began to sink, and as it slowly went down, the tree stumps, firmly anchored by their roots, went down with it. Water flowed around them and sand drifted over them, completely encasing the wood—some of the stone lay there on the mountainside still bearing the true markings of the bark. This quiet history of subsidence changed abruptly when an underwater volcano erupted and sent a great mass of black lava rolling over the trees and the sand that had enveloped them. At places the molten mass piled up to a depth of a thousand feet. In time quiet reigned again and the sand once more drifted in, and then there was another explosion. Five times this story was repeated, sand and lava and sand and lava again. The ocean that received such masses must have been profoundly deep, but again the subterranean forces exerted themselves and the bed of the sea was slowly but relentlessly uplifted into a mountain range more than seven thousand feet high. It was then that the winds and the rains and the snows began their work; over another great length of time they eroded away the upper layers of sandstone and lava until at last the petrified stumps stood forth bare and uncovered on the gaunt mountain slope where Charles Darwin found them.

"Vast and scarcely comprehensible as such changes must appear," Darwin wrote in his journal, "yet they have all occurred within a period recent when compared with the history of the Cordillera, and the Cordillera itself is absolutely modern as compared with many of the fossiliferous strata of Europe and America."

To substantiate his astounding story of the mountains, Darwin collected "half a mule's load" of specimens. As he said in a letter to his sister Susan, "without plenty of proof" he did not expect a word of his account to be believed.

In the most serious vein he wrote to Henslow: "If when you see my specimens, sections and accounts you should think that there is pretty strong presumptive evidence of the above facts, it appears very important; for the structure and size of this chain will bear comparison with any in the world and that all of this should have been produced in so recent a period is indeed wonderful."

Darwin's twenty-four-day crossing of the Andes ended with a pleasant ride south along the coastal plain to Santiago. It was April, the Chilean autumn; figs and peaches were spread out on cottage roofs to dry, and the men, women, and children were working in the vineyards. The scene was a "pretty one," but Darwin's thoughts were turning increasingly to England and it only made him miss the "pensive stillness" of the English autumn.

The *Beagle* lingered on the west coast of South America for another four months, making additional surveys in northern Chile and Peru. Darwin traveled into the northern Chilean mountains several times, but they were "tame" in comparison to the grandeur he had seen, and he tired of noting that the lowland country was "barren and sterile."

Peru was in a state of anarchy, with the President daily "shooting and murdering anyone who disobeyed his orders." Extensive traveling was impossible under the circumstances. On a few short trips Darwin stayed in houses so flea-ridden that he awakened in the morning almost freckled with bites.

Grumbling at this whole section of the world, which was stubbornly so unlike Shrewsbury, Darwin moved back on board the *Beagle*. His mood was not deeply unhappy, and after a few good dinners and some rest he was readily admitting that he was fatter and feeling fit. He was also quite willing to concede that there were two good things about Peru, its ladies and the fruit called the *chilimoya*, the Peruvian custard apple. The former, Darwin said, were as beautiful as the latter was delicious.

In Darwin's words, the ladies wore "elastic" gowns that fitted the figure very closely and obliged them to walk with "very small steps which they do very elegantly & display very white silk stockings and very pretty feet." Their black silk veils—mantillas—were brought over the head and held before the face in such a manner that only one eye remained uncovered, an eye "so black and brilliant and with such powers of expression that its effect is very powerful," Darwin testified. At twenty-six, the young Englishman felt as though he had been introduced to a number of "nice round mermaids" and he made no secret of the fact that he thought them much more worth looking at than the churches and buildings of Lima.

Only a few days remained before the *Beagle* would sail for the Galápagos. Well aware that it would be his last chance in many months to send letters off to England, Darwin wrote to friends and members of his family. Money was one point to be taken up in a letter home.

Susan was requested to tell her father that Charles had kept his promise of being extravagant in Chile. Earlier in the year he had drawn a bill for £100, half of which had gone to pay his expenses on the *Beagle* for a year. The expedition across the Andes had cost £60.

In the lighthearted mood of the moment, Charles added: "My father will believe that I *will* not draw money in crossing the Pacific because I *can* not. I verily believe that I could spend money on the moon. My travelling expenses are nothing; but when I reach a point such as Coquimbo, whilst my horses are resting, I hear of something very wonderful 100 miles off. A muleteer offers to take me for so many dollars & I cannot or rather never have, resisted the Temptation. My father's patience must be exhausted. . . . I write about it as a good joke, but upon my honor I do not consider it so."

Actually Dr. Darwin had made no complaints about his son's spending.

Three and a half years had passed since the *Beagle* had dropped anchor in the Brazilian port of Baía. In that time Charles Darwin had learned to see as no one before him had seen, and he had learned to question as no other had questioned. Backed by the incontrovertible evidence of his rock specimens, this young scientist, still in his twenties, had dared quietly and in no spirit of challenge to propose a wholly new history of the Andes. He had also formulated a bold new explanation for the origin of the differences in the animals of North and South America. He had gained too a vivid sense of the

great age of the earth and of the gradualness of its
changes.

Darwin was ready in a unique way for the still
greater surprises and the upsetting facts that the Galápagos held in store, though when the *Beagle* set sail
on September 7, 1835 he had only the faintest idea
of what awaited him.

The story of Darwin's determinative month in the
Galápagos is one that I have already told in the first
chapter of this book. His stay in the unusual islands completed his education for the great work of his life. When
he left he had his start.

On October 20, 1835 the *Beagle* sailed away from
the craterous Galápagos and turned her head toward
the South Seas, setting out on the long passage of thirty-
two hundred miles to Tahiti and the "right side" of the
world, the side that held the British Isles. The sun was
bright in a cloudless sky, and with her studding sails
set on both sides to catch the steady trade winds, she
sailed pleasantly, at the rate of about a hundred and fifty
miles a day, across the blue Pacific.

Clouds veiled the fabled beauty of Tahiti when the
Beagle came to anchor in her lagoon on November 15.
But as the clouds rolled away, the island stood revealed
in all its loveliness—the quiet lagoon, the long, shining
white beach, the precipitous central peaks, and all the
beautiful productions of the intertropical regions:
orange, banana, coconut, and breadfruit trees. Even the
brushwood bore a fruit, the guava.

Enchanted as he was by all this, Darwin was even
more pleased by the people. There was nothing of the
savage about them. On the contrary, their manner was

mild and pleasant, and their custom of working with the "upper part of the body quite naked" showed their tall, well-proportioned figures to great advantage. Even the tattooing with which they were decorated gracefully followed the body's curvature. Darwin thought the women's custom of wearing a white or scarlet flower in the hair was a very pretty one, but with the restraint of 1835 his only other comment was that they seemed to be in "greater want of some becoming costume even than the men."

That night in honor of the *Beagle's* arrival a great bonfire was lighted on the beach. As the English visitors and the Tahitians gathered around it, a little girl would sing a few impromptu verses telling of the ship, and the others would join in. As the haunting, "singular" music echoed through the palm trees and out across the moon-lit lagoon, Darwin was "unequivocally aware," with all the sense of differentness it implied, that he was at last in the South Seas. It was another and a lovely world.

Tahiti's towering central peak with its cascading waterfalls was an irresistible lure to a naturalist of Darwin's bent. He set out for the peak with his usual supplies lashed to a bamboo pole, which his two Tahitian guides slung over their shoulders. When they were urged to provide themselves with food and clothing they only laughed and explained that there would be plenty of food in the mountains and that their skins would do. The group climbed the steep mountain gorge, skirting the splashing, shining waterfalls. At a number of points the Tahitians would throw a rope around a projecting ledge and they all would clamber up. Darwin insisted that if the abyss they were edging had not been concealed by overhanging ferns and lilies he would never have dared this part of the climb.

That evening on a high ledge near a grove of wild mountain bananas, the Tahitians in a few minutes built Darwin a shelter of leaves. Then they folded pieces of fish, beef, ripe and unripe bananas, and the tops of the wild arum into green leaf parcels and placed them between hot stones. In a quarter of an hour a delicious dinner was ready.

From their position, almost suspended in space, the green valleys could be seen far below, while the lofty mountains, towering within sixty degrees of the zenith, hid half the evening sky. Content as men from the other side of the world seldom are, Darwin watched "the sublime spectacle" of the shades of night obscuring the last and highest pinnacles.

The sun was setting again behind the palms and peaks of this beautiful island as the *Beagle* sailed for New Zealand. Darwin stood at the rail, as travelers always have, reluctantly watching Tahiti recede into the night and the sea. And yet every league forward was a league nearer England. Darwin and Wickham took to calculating in an old atlas all the distances that lay ahead and estimating the date on which each leg of the long journey might be completed.

The *Beagle* tarried in New Zealand only the minimum time necessary, a bare ten days, and then sailed for Australia for a stay of a little less than three weeks. To a man longing intensely for England, the crude English settlements stood in sharp, disadvantageous contrast. Darwin also was shocked by the harsh treatment accorded the natives. It made him reflect that the varieties of man seemed to act on each other in the same way as different species of animals—the stronger always extirpating the weaker.

Darwin left the great under-continent with this salute: "Farewell Australia! You are a rising child, and doubtless some day will reign a great princess in the south, but you are too great and ambitious for affection, and yet not great enough for respect. I leave your shores without sorrow or regret."

The *Beagle* sailed on into the Indian Ocean and to Cocos, or Keeling Islands, which lay directly south of Sumatra. These form one of the many coral atolls which, to the bafflement of scientist and non-scientist alike, have everlastingly defied the power of the open ocean around them.

Inside the ring-shaped atoll lay the lagoon, its waters a vivid green in the vertical rays of the sun. Outside only a line of curling, frothing breakers separated the atoll from the heaving dark waters of the sea, and above only the level green tops of the coconut trees divided the little ring of land from the limitless blue vault of the heavens. A few white clouds flecked the azure of the sky, much as a few bands of living coral streaked the emerald waters of the lagoon.

Darwin had been fascinated by coral since he had first seen a few colorful specimens growing in the clear waters off Praia, in the Cape Verde Islands, and he had watched for the corallines all the way around South America. Even thoughts of England were forgotten as he and Captain Fitzroy waded, leaped, and vaulted to the outer edge of the reef. From that point, the ocean throwing its waters against the coral appeared even more of an invincible, all-powerful enemy. Darwin could see how in its storms it had torn loose great blocks of coral and tossed them onto the reef. And even on a day of quiet such as this one the long swell of the Pacific crashed at the first drag of the reef into breakers that almost anywhere else in the world would have been considered of gale force. It was impossible to look at the great oncoming walls of water and not to feel that an island, though built of porphyry, granite, or quartz, would ultimately be demolished. And yet the low coral islets stood intact and unbroken.

"Let the hurricane tear up its thousand huge fragments," Darwin wrote in his journal, "yet what will that tell against the accumulated labor of myriads of architects at work night and day, month after month? Thus do we see the soft and gelatinous body of a polypus, through the agency of the vital laws, conquering the great mechanical power of the waves of an ocean which neither the art of man nor the inanimate works of nature could successfully resist."

Only 2,200 yards from shore Captain Fitzroy dropped a sounding line 7,200 feet in length and found no bottom. In this way he and Darwin saw that the little atoll topped a submarine mountain with sides even steeper than those of the most abrupt volcanic cone.

Until Charles Darwin turned his observant eyes and questioning mind to the problem of the coral atoll, the most common assumption had been that the atolls were based on submarine craters. Darwin with his clear logic quickly disposed of that theory; Suadiva atoll was forty-four miles long in one direction and thirty-four in the other; Rimsky was fifty-four miles by twenty. Quite obviously no crater ever had such an oblong shape.

The captain and Darwin then covered their sounding

lead with prepared tallow and dropped it again and again
down the atoll's steep outer slope. Down to ten fathoms the tallow invariably came up marked with impressions of living coral; it was as clean as though it had
been dropped on a bare floor. As they went deeper and
deeper, though, fewer and fewer marks were made by
coral and the tallow picked up more and more sand. By
such careful measurements the two experimenters learned
that the coral polyps lived and constructed their branching reefs only within twenty to thirty fathoms (120 to
180 feet) of the surface.

The meaning of this living fact came quickly to Darwin: "Wherever there is now an atoll, a foundation
must originally have existed within a depth of from
twenty to thirty fathoms from the surface."

How was this foundation provided? It was impossible
to think, Darwin argued, that isolated steep-sided banks
of sediment could somehow have been deposited in the
profoundest, most limpid parts of the Pacific. There
were no rivers here to wash down the debris of the
land. It was also impossible to think that the "elevatory
forces" could have uplifted innumerable mountains to
within twenty or thirty fathoms of the surface with no
single pinnacle standing any higher. Where in the whole
globe was there a chain of mountains with all its sum-
mits rising to within a few feet of a given level?

If, then, the bases were not formed of sediment and
had not been uplifted, there could be only one answer.
They must, Darwin saw, have subsided. This theory at
once solved all the difficulties. As mountain after mountain slowly sank beneath the waves, fresh bases would be
successively provided for the growth of the corals. And
as the mountain continued to sink, the living corals

would continue building up to the surface and the waves that were their life.[1]

"We see in each atoll a monument over an island now lost," said Darwin. And he added: "We may thus gain some insight into the great system by which the surface of this globe has been broken up and the land and water interchanged."

The *Beagle* could at last turn definitely homeward. She stopped briefly at the island of Mauritius, off the coast of Madagascar, rounded the Cape of Good Hope, touched at the Atlantic island Ascension, and, to Darwin's near despair, sailed again for Baía, Brazil, to complete her chronometrical measurements of the world. The last task fortunately did not take long.

At dusk on October 2, 1836 the *Beagle* made the shores of England and dropped anchor in Falmouth harbor.

Five years and a world had passed since she had sailed out of Devonport on that gray December 27, 1831. In those five years the twenty-two-year-old amateur collector who had come aboard her with the new designation of naturalist had matured into a thorough and original-minded scientist.

The specimens and materials he had sent home ahead of him had aroused the interest of the scientists. Sedgwick, Darwin's former professor of geology, had called

[1] When American scientists in 1946 went out to Bikini atoll to prepare for the explosion of the atomic bomb, they established by borings and seismic soundings that the coral, living and dead, went down to a depth of about 7,000 feet. As the island had subsided, the coral had continued to build upward over a period that the scientists thought might have been twenty to thirty million years.

on Dr. Darwin to tell him that his son would take a place among the leading scientific men, and Henslow had read some of Darwin's letters before the Philosophical Society of Cambridge. The letters had been printed in a thirty-one-page pamphlet for distribution to members.

In Darwin's voluminous notes was the evidence to upset all the current beliefs about the origin of the Andes and of coral atolls, and to shake many another long-held theory about the living things of the world and their distribution. But it was another meaning that Charles Darwin was drawing from all he had seen which was to make this one of the most significant of all voyages.

The young naturalist returned convinced that the likenesses and differences of all living things were not matters of chance or of a creator's whim. Did this not mean, he was beginning to ask, that all the inhabitants of the world had descended from the same ancestors?

But this was for the future.

When Darwin stepped ashore on that early October evening in 1836 he was thinking only of home.

FIVE

THE FIRST–BORN

THE SUNDAY-NIGHT mail coach out of Falmouth
splashed and bumped over the rainy Cornwall roads.
One of the most uncomfortable passengers aboard was
Charles Darwin, who in his eagerness to get home had
engaged a place immediately after the *Beagle* had landed
at the old port at the southwest tip of England. Darwin
was feeling unwell and weak after several rough days at
sea, and the next day's jolting ride also was a bad one.
Only on Tuesday as the route turned north did Darwin begin to feel better, and did the fields and woods
and orchards of England begin to take on the gentle per-
vading beauty that he had been treasuring in his memory for the last five years. As they neared Shrewsbury
later in the day he was wondering, he said later, why
the stupid people on the coach did not think the fields
greener than any others and why they were not agog at
the rich cultivated land of England. But it was late at
night before the coach arrived at the ancient border
town of Shrewsbury, and, as he had planned if this should
be the case, Darwin went to the Lion, because he did
not want to arouse his family in the middle of the night.

The next morning before breakfast the traveler, home
from the seas, walked expectantly into The Mount.
Sisters, father, servants rushed excitedly around him. In
the melee of welcome and rejoicing, questions were asked
and the answers unheard; what mattered was that
Charles was home after five years looking fit though thin,

and that everyone at The Mount was well and de-
liriously happy to see him. Two laborers on the estate
capped the celebration that night by getting "roaringly
drunk."

At the first possible moment that day Charles dashed
off a note to his Uncle Jos, Josiah Wedgwood at Maer:
"My head is quite confused with so much delight. . . .
I am most anxious once again to see Maer and all its inhabitants so that in the course of two or three weeks, I
hope in person to thank you, as being my first Lord of the
Admiralty." He was, of course, referring to his uncle's
influential part in making the voyage possible for him.
Charles was grateful; the voyage had been wearyingly
long, but it had opened a new life to him. It had truly
been, as Uncle Jos had said, such an opportunity of seeing men and things as happens to only a few.

Many matters were immediately pressing for attention. Charles had to go to London within a few days
to get his "goods and chattels" out of the *Beagle,* and
he faced the additional problem of what to do about his
huge collections.

Word had reached him that Lyell had been following his reports and was eager to talk to him. Darwin
hurried to call on the noted geologist, both to express
his immeasurable appreciation for what Lyell's books
had meant to him, and to ask Lyell's advice about his
geological specimens. Lyell urged him to "work up" his
geological material himself.

Other "dons of science" both in London and Cambridge also welcomed Darwin. The young naturalist was
taken to dine at the Linnean and Geological Society
clubs and was promptly elected to membership in the
latter. Some scientists, however, were not so eager as

he had hoped to undertake the classification and dissection of his materials, he wrote his family.

All went so busily that not until the latter part of November was Charles able to make his promised visit to Maer. To welcome him home the whole family, including all the "outlyers," converged on the Wedgwood house. Only after Charles had been "unmercifully plied" with questions and the outlyers had gone could the immediate family settle down to serious talk about Charles's plans.

On the last leg of the voyage, when they were at Capetown, Captain Fitzroy had asked Charles to read him some portions of his journal. Evidently impressed, the Captain suggested that some of Darwin's notes might be incorporated in the books he was planning to write about the voyage. Darwin amiably agreed, if the Captain thought "the chit-chat details" of his journal worth publishing.

"We do not think Charles's journal should be mixed up with any work of the Captain's," objected Susan.

The whole family had been impressed with the parts of his journal that Charles had sent home, and Susan and Caroline, Charles's sisters, had insisted at once that it should be published separately. Both had gone to Maer with him, and there they picked up the argument again in the family discussions. Uncle Jos and Emma, as well as the others, agreed with them.

Charles had not forgotten his dream of writing a book of his own, and he was glad to accept their advice. He had previously planned to spend the next few months in Cambridge, putting his geological specimens in order. At Maer he decided that he would use as many evenings as possible to work on his journal. His father's original

plan for him to become a clergyman was so entirely forgotten that nothing more was heard of it.

It was good to be at Cambridge again, though a little
melancholy now that old classmates were gone. Darwin
worked hard, with considerable advice from Henslow,
at classifying and describing the big fossil bones he had
brought back from the pampas. He discovered that they
represented four new genera. Up to that time only two
genera of extinct South American mammals had been
described in England. One of the heads Darwin had dug
from the muds of the Argentine belonged to a gnawing
animal the size of a hippopotamus. Another was an anteater as large as a horse. The College of Surgeons was
happy to accept these important fossils and readily agreed
to make casts of them and to publish their descriptions.

Night after night as the *Beagle* had sailed around the
world Darwin had worked on his journal. He had written it so carefully and conscientiously, often from notes
jotted down in the little field notebooks he always carried with him, that there was little need for change. His
principal work was to recopy, recast, and expand some
of his original items, and to cut out other material that he
thought would not be of general interest. The original
journal consisted of about 189,000 words. About one
third of this he eliminated, principally comments on his
own feelings and notes about life on shipboard and his
shipmates. He added about 100,000 words, telling more
fully about some of the geological and zoological features of the countries he had visited. A few additional
personal details were put in, he said, to "make the hodge-
podge complete."

By spring Darwin saw that he would have to go to
London to complete his work. It had now been agreed

by all that his journal would be printed as a separate volume among the three volumes that were to be prepared on the voyage. Captain Fitzroy would be responsible for the first two. Darwin settled down in rooms at 36 Marlborough Street and continued the work on his journal.

Soon there was talk of another volume on the zoology of the voyage. The plan was for Darwin to bring together and publish the studies that various scientists were then making of his materials on fossil mammalia, recent mammalia, birds, fish, and reptiles. But a grant was needed to finance such a book. With considerable trepidation Darwin went to call on the Chancellor of the Exchequer, T. Spring-Rice, to ask for £1,000 for the zoological work. The Chancellor, as it turned out, was happy to meet the young naturalist. He appreciated the significance of his work and would make the money available. With a smile and a "make the most of it" he sent Darwin on his way.

The journal finally was ready for the printer early in the fall and came from the presses in November. Darwin sat that night in his room turning the first copy in his hands. "The smooth paper and the clear type has a charming appearance," he wrote to Henslow, "and I sat gazing in silent admiration at the first page of my own volume!"

Amused though he was at his own reaction, Darwin was exuberantly happy about the book, and he told Henslow: "If I live to be eighty I shall not cease to marvel at finding myself an author; in the summer before I started, if anyone had told me that I should have been an angel by this time, I should have thought it an equal impossibility."

The dark-blue volume that Darwin was examining was dedicated to Lyell "as an acknowledgment that the chief part of whatever scientific merit this journal and other works of the author may possess has been derived from studying the well-known and admirable *Principles of Geology*." More informally, Darwin said in a letter to Lyell: "My transformation into an author is all owing to you."

Actually the journal was not to be published for another two years, not until 1839. Publication was delayed by a wait for the first two volumes, which were coming from Fitzroy. In the meantime, however, Darwin sent a number of bound and unbound copies to friends and scientists he thought would be interested in it. They were more than interested, they were enthusiastic. Lyell's father wrote Darwin that he was delighted with every page. Although Darwin did not learn of it till some years afterward, Lyell sent a copy to Joseph Dalton Hooker, a young botanist, who was so excited about it that he slept with it under his pillow and planned how he too might go on such a voyage.

When publication finally came, Darwin's journal proved so much more popular than the first two volumes that it was soon reissued separately under the typically nineteenth-century title *Journal of Researches into the Geology and Natural History of the various Countries visited by H.M.S. Beagle under the command of Captain FitzRoy, R.N. From 1832 to 1836*. It came out later in the United States with the simpler title *The Voyage of the Beagle*.

Nothing ever pleased Darwin more, he said, than the success of his first "literary child." His reward, in the beginning at least, was not financial; it lay solely in the warm approval the book received. Several years later Darwin wryly pointed out in a letter to one of his sisters: "I reaped the other day all the profit I shall ever get from my Journal, which consisted in paying Mr. Colburn [the publisher] £21.10s for the copies which I presented to different people." Sales of the second edition, however, soon went to more than ten thousand.

Vile, smoky London—the adjectives were Darwin's —which so eagerly read young Mr. Darwin's book and began to draw him into her many activities, was alive with the brilliant turbulence that sometimes comes when the old and the new meet and are about to give rise to a distinctive new era. Everything was changing—economic life, social customs, the whole intellectual atmosphere—and a new queen, Victoria, was coming to the throne to give her name to the day that was dawning.

The new factories, spreading their long, dirty buildings and barracks-like workers' homes over surrounding fields, were challenging the agriculture on which the English economy had been based in the past. Some radicals were even proposing the repeal of the corn laws that had so long protected English produce. And the noisy new railroads that were tearing up the countryside, to the indignation of many old gentlemen, were not only about to doom the stagecoach but irrevocably to turn England into a world industrial power.

Almost daily at Maer the mail coach brought reports that the new railroad coming out to the west of England would soon be open. It was a hardy traveler, however, who would climb aboard one of the little coaches on wheels to be pulled across the country by the boiler-on-wheels locomotives that snorted so alarmingly through

their long funnel stacks. But in May 1836, when Emma
Wedgwood, Catherine Darwin, and a family party went
to Paris to meet their Aunt Jessie and her husband, the
noted Swiss historian J. C. de Sismondi, they took the
railroad from Birmingham to Rugby. The journey, in
all probability their first, was made in the remarkable
time of two and a half hours—the distance was about
thirty miles—and they discovered with pleasure and surprise that this part of their trip was less fatiguing than
the earlier coach ride. Emma was so impressed that she
urged her Aunt Harriet Surtees, who was meeting them
later, to take the railroad "after all."

In the seething change of the day the very bases and
concepts on which life was lived were being called into
question and re-examined. The questioning extended
from a reverent, anxious doubting of orthodox religion
to a revolt against the traditional parceling out of church
posts to those with aristocratic connections or family influence. It was part of this latter system that had nearly
pushed Charles Darwin into a "living" in the church.
Passage of the great Reform Bill of 1832 had evened
out the inequalities in wealth within the church, but it
did not bring an end to the dissenting question that was
applied to every institution from church to rotten bor-
ough: of what use is it? It was this atmosphere that
gave birth and meaning to writers like Carlyle and Rus-
kin, and that opened the way for the social satire of
Dickens, Thackeray, and Trollope. This climate of
searching and doubt also made the historian who could
supply the perspective for which the era cried, a man
writing not for scholars alone but for people generally,
and ultimately it made possible Charles Darwin.

As a man who had looked at new worlds and raised

new questions, Darwin was part of this intellectual revolution. He belonged to it, and it was inevitable that he should meet the others who were giving it life and movement.

Soon after Charles came to London, his brother Erasmus took him one Sunday to drink tea with the Carlyles. Erasmus had long since established himself in London, where he led the life of a gentleman in both the literal and the occupational sense of the word. He too had early side-stepped his father's plan to make him a physician. In London Erasmus moved graciously in society, read extensively, collected a fine library, and acted as something of a patron of the arts. He eased the life of his close friends, the financially hard-pressed Carlyles, in many ways, one being to place his carriage at their disposal.

On the Sunday when Charles met the famous Scot his first feeling was that "one must always like Thomas." Jenny, however, spoke such a broad Scottish accent that Charles missed about half of what she said. The three met a number of times at Erasmus's house and at family parties, and Darwin found Carlyle's talk "racy and interesting, just like his writings," but endless.

Carlyle's noted conversational sweep all but wrecked one party that Erasmus gave. Erasmus had planned a distinguished little dinner at which the guests were Carlyle, Lyell, Charles Babbage, professor of mathematics at Cambridge and also a noted writer, and Charles. As they sat down to dinner Carlyle seized the floor with a harangue on the advantages of silence and never yielded it. After dinner Babbage, who was as fond of talking as Carlyle, thanked him in his grimmest manner for his lecture on silence.

Charles was invited to meet Macaulay at Lord Stanhope's, where the historians frequently gathered. This dinner went very well; Macaulay, unlike some of his contemporaries, "did not talk too much." Darwin always remembered with pleasure a little story Stanhope told him. At dinner Macaulay and the other historians often would get into a dispute about some date or fact. Generally someone would leave the table and go to the library to track it down. After a while, though, they ceased to take the trouble. Any date or fact that Macaulay supplied required no checking; it invariably was right.

Darwin was wholly in the spirit of the day, but he could not stand the tempo. Dinners and meetings, with the kind of battling that often went on—Carlyle denouncing Grote's *History* as a "fetid quagmire with nothing spiritual in it"—exhausted him. He would be seriously ill with a bad headache the next day. Even quiet social affairs with close friends and relatives proved a strain. Anything that "flurried" him "knocked" him up badly. He tried to withdraw as much as possible from social life, but even so, he several times had to flee to the peace of the country to recuperate.

Charles was thinking increasingly about getting away from the city permanently. He also was thinking more and more about his cousin Emma Wedgwood and about marriage.

He jotted down the advantages of marriage—children, if it pleased God, a constant companion, charms of music, female chitchat. In another column he listed the disadvantages—terrible loss of time, if many children forced to gain one's bread, fighting about not going out in society. After weighing the two he concluded: "My

God, it is intolerable to think of spending one's whole
life like a neuter bee, working, working, and nothing
after all. No, no, won't do. . . . Imagine living all
one's days solitarily in smokey dirty London. . . .
Only picture to yourself a nice soft wife on sofa, with a
good fire and books and music perhaps . . . compare
this vision with the dingy reality of Gt. Marlboro' St."
Then he firmly wrote: "Marry, marry, marry."

Shortly afterward Darwin made a special trip to Maer
to ask Emma to be his wife. She had been hoping for
such a moment since his return from the voyage, but did
not dare to feel that his gentle manner to her was any
more than his normally affectionate way with all those
he loved. Their engagement was greeted with great joy
by both families. Several years before, Charles's sister
Caroline had married Josiah Wedgwood III, and this
further linking of the two closely knit families seemed
inevitable and desirable to all of them. Josiah Wedgwood, Uncle Jos, wrote to Dr. Darwin: "I could have
parted with Emma to no one for whom I would so soon
and so entirely feel as a father, and I am happy in believing that Charles entertains the kindest feelings for
his uncle-father."

Uncle Jos added that he proposed to do for Emma
what he had done for his daughter Charlotte and three
of his sons on their marriages. He would present her with
a £5,000 bond and an income of £400 a year "as long
as my income will supply it, which I have no reason for
thinking will not be as long as I live."

Charles's happiness, as their wedding was set for
January 1839, was deep and clear, though he worried
that Emma might find quiet evenings with him dull
after having lived all of her life "with such large and

agreeable parties as only Maer can boast of." "Dear, dear Emma," he wrote, "I positively can think of nothing but you. . . ."

Emma was a woman as gentle, as devoted, and as unswerving as the man she was to marry and whom she knew so well: "He is the most transparent man I ever saw and every word expresses his real thoughts."

Emma had been born on May 8, 1808, nine months before Charles. She and her sister Fanny, two years older, were the youngest of the nine Wedgwood children. They were inseparable, the "dovelies," the pets of that large and happy household. Emma was principally educated at home in the liberal Wedgwood tradition. Children were not to be forbidden or scolded or preached to, but neither were parents or governesses to yield to a child's commands or caprice. Emma picked up some French and German on several visits abroad and played the piano with more than the usual skill. But her great gift lay in caring for others. Even as a young woman she was "a rock to lean on, her self-command never gave way," as one of her relatives said.

At the time of her engagement to Charles Darwin, Emma was a tall, slender, more than ordinarily attractive woman of thirty. Her shining brown hair was parted in the center and drawn into two soft clusters of curls at either side of her face. Her features were firm and clear-cut—it was thus that George Richmond painted her at about this time—and she retained this cleanness of form and line throughout her life; there was never any fleshiness or heaviness about her.

She had an easygoing disposition, with no talent either for "tidiness" or for clothes. Her sisters and relatives always thought it their duty to see that Emma paid some attention to fashion. Her Aunt Jessie, Mme de Sismondi, in writing her heartfelt good wishes on her niece's engagement also begged her to "pay a little more" for her clothes and not to despise "those little cares which give everyone more pleasing looks."

Charles, not long before, had been persuaded much against his wishes to become secretary of the Geological Society. His duties to the society, in addition to his work on the zoological report of the *Beagle*, would, he felt, compel him and Emma to live in London for a while after their marriage. He and Erasmus drove and walked the streets of the city looking for a suitable house; the landlords all had gone mad, they asked such prices. At last they found a house at 12 Upper Gower Street which in addition to its front drawing-room boasted a quieter rear one looking out on a little garden. The garden was just big enough for "a mouthful of air," but for London was better than no garden at all.

The house had yellow curtains that made Charles wince every time he saw them, and the other furnishings ran such a riot of color that he nicknamed the house "Macaw Cottage." Relatives assisted him in engaging a butler, cook, and maids, and on January 1 Charles moved in with two vanloads of goods, mostly geological specimens. He wrote Emma that everything had arrived safely except the few dozen drawers of shells which would have to be carried over by hand.

For the wedding at Maer, Charles's tailor was trying to persuade him to order a blue coat and white trousers. At this he balked, insisting that he would wear only clothes in which he could "decently travel." The coat he chose was cut with wide notched lapels and the waistcoat was in the same style. His high collar jutted well up above the jawline and with it was worn a wide, knotted cravat. Even in his new wedding clothes Charles was convinced that he made such a poor appearance that he wondered at Emma's willingness to marry him. Emma, and others far less biased than she, thought to the contrary. At thirty Charles was so slender his broad shoulders seemed to stoop a little. His light-brown hair was brushed back from his exceptionally wide forehead and worn long at the sides, in the fashion of the day. His eyes were deep-set under heavy overhanging brows.

Charles and Emma were quietly married in the Maer church on January 29, 1839. They went immediately afterward to their new home in Gower Street, which they found "blazing with fires" and looking comfortable and welcoming.

Invitations poured in from the Lyells, from relatives and other friends. Although they did no more than they had to, the strain soon proved too much for Charles. Even after a quiet dinner with friends he would awaken the next day with a severe headache and nausea. Before the year was over he was seriously ill. Emma was pregnant and not well either, and they began to live very quietly, even by their standards.

Their first child, William Erasmus, was born on December 27, 1839, the eighth anniversary of the sailing of the *Beagle*. Of all fond young parents, Charles Darwin was surprised—though no one else was—to find himself one of the fondest. The baby, nicknamed Mr. Hoddy Doddy, was "so charming" that his father could not pretend to any modesty about him. "I defy anybody to flatter us," he wrote happily to a relative, "for I defy anyone to say anything in his praise of which we are not fully conscious."

Although he was seldom able to get in a full day of work, for his illness continued, Darwin completed his supervisory work on the zoology of the *Beagle* and pushed ahead on a new book on coral reefs. In the latter book he wanted to present in more detail the amazing theory of the formation of coral reefs which he had developed on the voyage.

As he rechecked his work on the coral reefs, he could detect no errors in his theory; it had been cautiously and carefully formed. But there was one final test that could be applied to it. If he was right in thinking that atoll and barrier reefs were formed in areas of subsidence, there should be no volcanoes near them, for volcanic action is associated with an upthrusting of the earth's crust. And if, on the other hand, he was right in believing that fringing reefs, reefs not divided from the land by a deep channel, had been built on a rising base, there should be volcanoes in their vicinity. Darwin decided to apply this test to all the world's reefs and volcanoes.

For months, whenever he was able, he worked at the Admiralty and the British Museum, poring over old charts, sailing directions, and narratives of voyages. On a big map he colored all the reported atolls a deep turquoise blue, and all the barrier reefs a light aqua blue. He made all the fringing reefs a rich coral color, and dotted in all the known volcanoes with vermilion. Would any vermilion dots appear in the blue areas? It was an anxious question as his very beautiful map took on its new colors.

There were a few complications, to be sure, for the ever varying earth never permits a perfect demonstration, but in the arching curve of turquoise atolls stretching

from the South Seas through the Carolines and almost
to the Philippines, there was not a single vermilion dot.
And it was the same in the Indian Ocean; no volcanoes
thrust up their cones near the coral atolls there. But off
the coast of Sumatra and along the Philippines, where
the coral-colored fringing reefs extended over great areas,
vermilion dot after vermilion dot appeared. The world's
map overwhelmingly supported Darwin's theory of the
coral reefs. A copy of this handsome map was placed in
his book *The Structure and Distribution of Coral Reefs,*
which was completed in 1842.

The gelatinous, insignificant little coral polyps end-
lessly building their mountainous, branching reefs provided also a "grand and harmonious picture of the movements of the earth." They were a gauge showing that
vast areas had been upraised by the irresistible seething
of molten forces deep within the earth. And they showed
with equal clarity that other areas had been sinking
slowly and gradually.

And Darwin added: "We may feel sure that the
movement has been so slow as to have allowed the coral
to grow up to the surface, and so widely extended as to
have buried over the broad face of the ocean every one
of those mountains above which an atoll now stands."

The coral told the story of the earth.

By the time this small, though momentous, book was
published, Darwin knew that he would have to find
a way to lead a quieter life. London, odious anyhow to
one who loved the country, made it extremely difficult to
stay away from overtaxing social demands. Charles and
Emma wanted urgently to find a house in the country
where they would be removed from the pressure of London and yet would be close enough for Charles to keep

in touch with friends and to come in occasionally for
scientific meetings.

This led them to Down. Down, a large country house,
was in Kent, only sixteen miles by direct line from London Bridge, but a twenty-mile drive by coach, part of
the way through lanes so narrow the trees met overhead.
It was difficult to pass a cart without waiting to reach a
wide place in the road. Darwin laughingly denied a
statement once made in a German publication that his
house could only be approached by mule track, yet he
acknowledged that it stood in the most perfectly quiet
country he had ever seen.

The village of Downe, a quarter of a mile away, consisted of nothing more than a few houses clustered
around an old flint church. In the other direction lay
only great woods and arable fields. No gentleman's
house or village had ever been built between Down
House and the edge of the escarpment that separated
the high chalk flat on which Down stood and the lower
part of Kent. The rolling, uninterrupted view in this
direction always gave Darwin a feeling, he said, of living on the edge of the world.

The valleys near Down were odd; not even the
tiniest streams furrowed their rounded bottoms, for in
this chalk country the water drained immediately away.
When Charles and Emma first saw this country in the
winter of 1842 it looked bleak. Later they thought it
rich in any season of the year, and particularly in the
spring, when violets turned the slopes into purple car-
pets of bloom.

Darwin bought eighteen acres of land along with the
big square three-story brick house. It had a "capital
study," eighteen by eighteen, well lighted by windows

that ran all the way to the floor. The living-room, Charles and Emma saw at once, could be enlarged, and upstairs there were numerous bedrooms, enough to accommodate even a combined party of Darwins and Wedgwoods. After a bay wing was added, there were even more.

Within a few years Darwin had wide lawns surrounding the house and had put in flower beds that extended close to the windows. There was a fine row of lime trees and handsome planting that screened the garden from all outside view. To one side lay the kitchen garden and later the greenhouse where Darwin carried on his experimental work and the entrance to the sand walk. The sand walk was an essential part of Down; it bordered an acre and a half of woods and open country with a lovely view across a shallow valley. Here Darwin walked almost every day.

Down was a house that the Darwins made completely their own and came to love dearly. And here they lived for the remainder of their lives.[1]

[1] Down House is now a national possession. Largely through the efforts of Sir Arthur Keith, a president of the British Association, Sir Buckston Browne purchased, restored, and endowed Down House for the nation. At an impressive ceremony in 1929 it was turned over to the care of the British Association. Two years later Sir Buckston purchased the fields adjoining the sand walk, and, as an additional memorial to Charles Darwin, there built and endowed a research station for young surgeons.

SIX

COINCIDENCE AND CLASH

CHARLES DARWIN slowly and thoughtfully examined the big fossil bone he held in his hands. It was the head of the giant anteater he had dug from the earth of South America; it was different from any living anteater, and yet, he noted in his diary, it was connected in some of the most "singular and complex" ways with the modern species. It must have been an ancient ancestor of the existing anteaters.

This brought old and deeply troublesome questions flooding back into his mind. If this huge extinct animal that he had found in the pampas muds was truly the ancestor of the living forms, then one species surely had given rise to another. And that could only mean that each had not been separately, miraculously created. It was at Cambridge in 1837 that Darwin at last frankly faced this disturbing, revolutionary thought, he said in his autobiography.

A few weeks later in London, as he worked over his Galápagos materials, he was confronted once more with the wonderful and undeniable similarities of species. It still looked as though one species, say the giant tortoises, had been modified into different species when the animals were separated geographically on the various islands of the archipelago. Here was another inescapable instance of one species dividing into others, and in not too remote a time.

So, putting aside his doubts and his scruples, Darwin wrote "Transmutation of Species" at the head of a little notebook. And he began to jot down some of the thoughts that came to him: "Propagation explains why modern animals same type as extinct, which is law almost proved."

In his diary he made a note of what he had done: "In July opened first notebook on Transmutation of Species. Had been greatly struck from about the month of previous March with character of South American fossils and species on Galapagos Archipelago. These facts (especially the latter) origin of all my views."

Darwin was working at the time on his journal and on the zoological report of the voyage, but the subject of species "haunted" him, he said. The problem, however, seemed overwhelming. To go into it at all, he wrote in his new notebook, would involve digging into comparative anatomy—there would be new zest to that if he were right. It would mean plunging into a study of instincts and heredity, and of "mind heredity," and, in fact, of the whole of metaphysics. An investigation of hybrids would certainly be necessary, and of what causes change, "in order to know what we have come from and to what we tend." Unquestionably there would have to be an examination of species.

As he wavered before the immensity of the task he was outlining for himself, Darwin revealed in his autobiography, he thought of Lyell and of how he had begun by indiscriminately collecting all the facts on geologic change. Perhaps if he collected all the facts that bore in any way on the variation in animals and plants under domestication and nature, "some light might be thrown on the whole subject."

With this procedure in mind, and working, as he liked to think, on "the true Baconian principle" of collecting all facts without regard to theory, Darwin started to gather material on a wholesale scale. He subscribed to breeders' journals and catalogues and read everything he could get on the subject. He overlooked no source of information.

He wrote to his cousin William Darwin Fox, who had been at Cambridge with him and whose college interest in beetles had matured into a lively concern with breeding. Species, Darwin explained, had become his prime hobby "and I really think that some day I shall be able to do something in that most intricate subject, species and varieties." Later Darwin wrote to Fox again: "I continue to collect all kinds of facts about 'Species and Varieties' for my someday work to be so entitled; the smallest contributions thankfully accepted. . . ."

Darwin specified that he would like to have descriptions of all crosses between all domestic birds and animals, dogs, cats, and so on. And if Fox's half-bred African cat should die, he would be very much obliged if its carcass could be sent to him in a little hamper. Darwin added that any cross-bred pigeons, fowl, or ducks would be more acceptable than the finest haunch of venison.

After a relatively short study of what the breeders were doing, Darwin was convinced that selection was the key to man's success in making useful races of animals and plants. The breeder of race horses did not mate his fastest horse indiscriminately with other horses; he selected the two fleetest and thereby hoped to produce a superior offspring. But in nature, where there was no breeder with a record book, how could selection work? Darwin said in his autobiography that he puzzled long about this difficult problem.

It remained "a mystery" to him for some months, until in October 1838 he happened to read "for amusement" the already famous book of Thomas Malthus on *Population*. Malthus was warning that if the human population of the earth continued to increase unchecked, it ultimately would outrun its food supply; only war, disease, and famine were holding down the increase and preventing such a catastrophe. Malthus emphasized the ruthless, continuous struggle going on in nature. Darwin, as he said, was "well prepared" to understand that, and perhaps with a vividness possible to few others. In South America he had seen the prickly cardoon taking over hundreds of square miles, choking out all other growth. In New Zealand he had watched the white settlers "extirpating" the natives. Everywhere that he had looked there had been an intense struggle for life and survival.

"It at once struck me," Darwin wrote in his autobiography, "that under these circumstances the most favourable variations would tend to be preserved and the unfavourable ones destroyed." The struggle itself was the selective agent! And as the best-adapted survived and the others went to extinction, the survivors would inevitably differ from their ancestors. In the end new species would develop.

"I had at last got a theory by which to work," he said.

Darwin had all the essential pieces; his theory held together logically, and yet it was so radical and so at variance with all the prevailing thought that he decided he should not then attempt to write it down. He would think about it and test it in every way possible.

Not until June 1842, a few months before he and

Emma moved to Down, did he "allow" himself "the satisfaction" of writing a brief abstract of it. He did it in pencil, and when he finished, his copy ran to thirty-five pages.

Several years before, in 1839, Darwin had been walking in Trafalgar Square. Purely by chance he met an officer who had been with him on the *Beagle,* and with the officer a strikingly handsome young man, Joseph Dalton Hooker, the son of Sir William Hooker, director of the Royal Botanical Gardens at Kew. Darwin soon forgot this casual encounter, but Hooker always remembered it. It was at this time that he was sleeping with the proofs of Darwin's *Journal* under his pillow and hurrying with his studies so that he could volunteer to go with Sir James Ross on his forthcoming expedition to the Antarctic. He hoped to follow in the footsteps of the tall young man he was meeting, "the man with the animated expression, the mellow voice, the beetling brows and the sailor-like—frank and cordial—greeting of his old friend."

In the fall of 1839 Hooker sailed south with Ross, almost on the track of the *Beagle.* Beyond Darwin's Tierra del Fuego, however, H.M.S. *Erebus,* Ross's ship, entered the polar ice pack in an attempt to locate the south magnetic pole. Later, on her way back to England, she anchored one night under a black precipice where the *Beagle* once had stopped. "A more extraordinary anchorage for wildness and sublimity we never lay at," said Hooker. "Indeed all Mr. Darwin's remarks are so true and so graphic that Mr. Lyell's present [Darwin's *Journal*] is not only indispensable but a delightful companion and guide."

Hooker, who had been trained in botany from his childhood, returned from the three-year voyage of the *Erebus* an expert botanist. He was soon to be acknowledged as one of the world's authorities in his field. Darwin had read some of Hooker's voyage letters—Lyell had passed them along to him—and, soon after Hooker's return, wrote him a warm letter of congratulation on his "long and glorious voyage." At the first opportunity Darwin invited the young botanist to have breakfast with him at Erasmus's house in London. Hooker soon afterward visited Darwin at Down. When he volunteered to study Darwin's collection of Tierra del Fuego and Galápagos plants, Darwin was delighted. He was even more "delighted and astonished" when Hooker's study supported his views on the differences in the plants from the different islands, a point about which he said he had "always been fearful."

It was thus that a lifelong friendship and close working association began. Whenever Darwin required expert botanical advice, he turned to Hooker. He received not only the information he needed, but support, constructive criticism, and an understanding that gave him courage to go on with work to which nearly all other scientists were contemptuously opposed. Darwin was, above all, the non-specialist, the man whose eyes were on the wholes, the total patterns and meanings; Hooker was pre-eminently the master of one field. But they were men of like mind and, as Darwin once said, co-circumnavigators of the globe, and both sensed almost from the beginning of their long friendship how rarely they complemented each other.

As early as January 1844 Darwin took Hooker into his confidence: "I have been now ever since my return

engaged in a very presumptuous work and I know no
one individual who would not say a very foolish one. I
was so struck with the distribution of the Galapagos
organisms &c., &c., and with the character of the American fossil mammifers &c. &c., that I determined to collect blindly every sort of fact which could bear in any
way on what are species. . . . At last gleams of light
have come, and I am almost convinced (quite contrary
to the opinion I started with) that species are not (it is
like confessing a murder) immutable."

The die was cast. That summer Darwin enlarged his
brief 1842 species sketch to a statement of two hundred
and thirty pages. He had it copied out and sent a copy to
Hooker with the request that he read it and return it. It
was divided into two parts: "I. On the variation of
Organic Beings under Domestication and in their Natural State"; and "II. On the Evidence favourable and
opposed to the view that Species are naturally formed
races descended from common Stocks." Here was much
of the theory later made famous in the *Origin of Species*.

But there was other work to be done too; species
could not pre-empt all of his time. Darwin took great
pains in correcting and revising a new edition of the
Journal which came out in 1845. Despite recurring illness he also worked for a period of four and a half years
on his three geological books, *Coral Reefs, Volcanic Islands,* and *Geological Observations on South America.*

When at last this long grind was finished and the
South American Observations came out in 1846, Darwin was "over-done," ill, and weary. But in the ten
years that had passed since the *Beagle's* return to England, all of his materials had been studied and reported

on. The *Journal*, the zoological studies, and the three
geological books told the whole fresh story as Darwin
had seen it unfold before him in the five years when the
Beagle circled the earth. Everything was complete,
everything was accounted for; that is, everything except
one little specimen. Only one tiny barnacle remained.

Darwin was skinning his shins and his hands on the
rocks along the rough Chonos archipelago off the coast
of southern Chile back in 1834 when he found the
curious barnacle. Instead of clinging, as all good barnacles should have, this little specimen, no larger than the
head of a pin, was burrowing into a mollusk shell. Check
as he would, Darwin could find no other like it; he had
to set up a whole new sub-order for it.

Darwin was eager to get on with his species work—
he had written Hooker: "Hurrah now for my species
work"—but perhaps, he said, he should first study the
odd Chilean barnacle. That would mean examining and
dissecting hundreds of other barnacles, an onerous, weari-
some job. Perhaps, though, he wrote to Hooker, no one
had a right to discuss species until he had thoroughly
mastered one and worked out "his due share." So Darwin dug in, and, once started, he could no more let go
than one of his barnacles. He worked for a solid eight
years and ultimately published two thick volumes describing all known living species and two thin quartos
on extinct species. He knew, he said, that Bulwer-
Lytton had him in mind when in one of his novels he
caricatured a Professor Long who had written two huge
volumes on limpets.

Almost every morning Darwin was at the dissecting-
board that had been "let into" the embrasure of one

window of his study. Although dissection and work with the miscroscope was difficult for him, he spent day after day at it, attempting to classify the minute animals he was studying. The names that had been given to the different species were so meaningless they almost drove him to despair. Even on the basis of structure it was extremely difficult to classify the various species. Darwin would decide after weeks of work that one set of forms constituted a distinct species, only to examine them again and tear up his manuscript to make them separate. And then he would make them one again.

"I have gnashed my teeth, cursed species and asked what sin I committed to be so punished," he wrote to Hooker in one wry moment of frustration.

One of the children, on a visit to a neighbor's house, looked all around for a study equipped with a microscope and other scientific apparatus. When he saw none, he asked: "Then where does Mr. —— do his barnacles?" He assumed that barnacles were part of every home.

Actually the long labor with *Cirripedes*—barnacles— gave Darwin the same kind of thorough firsthand knowledge of anatomy that the voyage of the *Beagle* had given him in the field of geology. He learned by his grueling work, much of it similar to a postgraduate's training today, how much of a "speculative strain" he could later place on biological facts. He learned too how unreliable classifications are, and how stubbornly biological data can vary. Hooker always told Darwin that he had never done a wiser thing than to devote himself to the toil on barnacles.

All the while, life at Down went on with a calmness, evenness, and understanding that lightened any work, and in Darwin's case, where the balance between health

and ill-health was precarious, the ordered peace was all
that made possible his amazing accomplishment. Life
at Down was an idyll, Victorian in time, un-Victorian
in its gentleness and lack of sternness or formality.

Most of the children were born in this big country
house: Henrietta in 1843, George in 1845, Elizabeth
in 1847, Francis in 1848, Leonard in 1850, and Horace
in 1851. William, the former Mr. Hoddy Doddy, came
there as a three-year-old. The Darwins lost two other
children in infancy and Anne, who was born in 1841, at
the age of ten.

To all of them Down was a place compounded of
sunshine and happiness. Henrietta, long after she was
grown, thought and wrote of it in the sweet terms of a
summer day, with the rattle of the flywheel of the well
as it drew water for the garden, of lilies, phlox, and
larkspur blooming in the long beds in front of the drawing-room windows, of bees humming in the lime trees,
of her father lying on the grass, of children playing, and
of her mother dressed in lilac muslin watching over the
whole lovely scene. There was an unworldly, dreamlike
perfection about it, but so it was.

Many years later Gwen Darwin Raverat, the granddaughter of Charles and Emma, was to explain: "Sometimes it almost seems that life at Down must have been
too happy and the relations between parents and children too perfect; for the uncles [Darwin's five sons]
never seemed quite to get away from that early Elysium,
or quite to belong to the ordinary horrid world."

Emma's life was fitted entirely to Charles's. Her time
was arranged so that she could be with him in all of his
free hours. In sickness she was constantly at his side,

sitting by the hour in darkened rooms as he lay prostrate with severe headaches, always solicitous, never impatient, guarding his health and peace with unending, tender care.[1] Charles's love for her grew deeper with the years, and discord was unknown between them.

Darwin always said that there was only one time when Emma was cross with him. She loved the wild flowers that grew along the sand walk and always had a boy pull out the dog's mercury and the jack-in-the-hedge to encourage the growth of the bluebells, the primroses, the cowslips, and particularly the wild ivy. One boy, however, misunderstood his orders. When Charles and Emma reached the walk that day, they found bare earth and a towering pile of wild ivy torn out by its roots. The hated dog's mercury flourished untouched. One glance at Emma's face was too much for Charles. He burst out laughing. On top of the earlier tragedy this was too much for Emma.

Darwin was up early each morning and out for a walk before breakfast. Often one of the children would join him; Francis could recall walking with his father in the red light of a winter sunrise and feeling "the honour and glory in it." Darwin liked to tell the children too how once or twice he had met foxes trotting home at dawn.

After breakfasting alone at 7:45, he went to his study to work. The hour and a half between 8:00 and 9:30 was one of his most productive working times.

[1] Douglas Hubble in his article in the *Lancet*, Dec. 26, 1953, said: "Nursing was Emma Darwin's métier. . . . In the Wedgwood enjoyment of sickness lay the emollient influence that fixed irreversibly Charles Darwin's hypochondriacal habit. The perfect nurse had married the perfect patient."

At 9:30 he went down to the drawing-room for the
mail, and while he rested on the sofa Emma would
read aloud any family letters, or perhaps from a novel.
At 10:30 Darwin went back to his study to work until
noon. Sometimes if a child was sick and would promise
to be very quiet he could lie on the study sofa while his
father worked, and sometimes the children would run in
and out for a piece of paper or some sticking-tape or
something of the kind, but generally he was undisturbed.
By noon Darwin felt that he had done a good day's
work and he was ready for his midday walk.

With Polly, his rough-haired fox terrier, or one of
her predecessors accompanying him, he usually stopped
at the greenhouse to see how his experimental plants
were coming along and then took a turn either around
the sand walk or along one of the many footpaths that
followed the ridges of the Down country. The children
nearly always were playing along the sand walk and in
the acre-and-a-half lot that it enclosed. Darwin would
join in their games as he went along, and they would
run along with him to see some special bird or flower.
Once when he was collecting all the grasses of the vicinity the children became collectors too. Darwin was fond
of telling how one of the boys found a grass that he had
not seen before and, putting it beside his father's plate
at dinner, told him: "I are an extraordinary grass finder."

Luncheon was served after the midday walk. Afterward Darwin went back to the drawing-room to read
the paper, almost the only non-scientific reading he did
for himself. Everything else was read to him to relieve
him of a strain that seemed to contribute to his exhaustion and headaches. A big horsehair chair was then
pulled up beside the fire, and with a writing-board across

its arms Darwin would attend to his correspondence. He had many long letters to write. Occasionally he would dictate them to one of the family from rough notes he had made, generally on the back of other letters. When the letters were finished Emma would read aloud again, and if Charles dropped off to sleep she would continue lest the cessation of the sound might awaken him.

Charles worked again from 4:30 to 5:30. After dinner he and Emma always had a game of backgammon. They kept a running score and made a great show of wanting to keep ahead. If his strength would allow it, he would read for a while, but if not Emma would again read aloud to him or would play the piano. About ten o'clock Darwin went to his room, though he frequently was unable to sleep and would sit up in bed for hours going over and over some scientific problem that was troubling him.

Occasionally relatives came to visit, and sometimes the Hookers, Lyells, or other scientific friends. There were a few trips to a water cure that seemed to do him good, and a few visits to the seashore, but such absences from Down were few. Darwin went to London so seldom—his coachman on these occasions drove him ten miles to the nearest railroad station—that he felt he was losing touch with the scientific societies and should go more often. He scarcely knew the younger members and he looked changed to the older ones. At forty-five Darwin was becoming quite bald; the top of his head was bare, and only a fringe of dark hair remained around the sides of his head. His side whiskers, however, were long and luxuriant. He still wore a high, flaring collar and a wide, large-knotted cravat. With his checked waistcoat and his "fresh and blooming" country com-

plexion, he looked very much the country gentleman.[2]
"Squire," his pigeon-fancier friends used to call him.
There was no question about his attachment to the
country. He left Down reluctantly for even short jaunts
and returned to it with relief and gladness.

The barnacle work was finally finished in the summer
of 1854, after eight long years. When the last two volumes came out, it was with a feeling of good riddance
that Darwin began sending "10,000 barnacles out of the
house." In September he wrote Hooker that within a
day or two he would begin to look over his old notes on
species.

The species problem had never been dropped, but
now in September 1854 Darwin took it up intensively.
He stepped up his correspondence and reading, and he
experimented widely on dozens of the problems involved. He wrote Hooker that "in a year or two's time"
he might be ready to write. There was some discussion
of his publishing a preliminary sketch of his views, but
both Hooker and Lyell advised against this course. Both
urged Darwin to write a book in which he could fully
present his ideas with all the material to back them up,
and they urged him to hurry with it. In 1857 twenty
years had passed since Darwin had opened his first notebook on species. In the big portfolios into which he
slipped materials was an enormous accumulation of data
on biology, geology, botany, and half a dozen other
branches of science. Spurred on by the twenty-year anniversary as well as by his friends, Darwin began to pull
his material together and to write. But there was always

[2] Darwin once wrote to Hooker: "Everyone tells me that I
look quite blooming and beautiful, and most think I am sham-
ming, but you have never been one of those."

another problem that needed investigation. Early in 1858 he had finished only eleven chapters, and he told friends that the subject was "so very long" that he did not think that he could possibly go to press for another two years at least. Perhaps he would never have been wholly ready, for his subject, life itself, was limitless.

And then the unbelievable happened.

On June 18, 1858, as Darwin opened his morning mail, out of it fell an essay by Alfred Russel Wallace, an English naturalist then living in Malaya, with whom Darwin had been corresponding.

It was called "On the Tendency of Varieties to depart indefinitely from the Original Type." As Darwin read he was stunned. There in a few pages was all of his theory, all of it. If Wallace had had his 1844 sketch he could not have made a better brief abstract of it. Even his terms stood as the heads of Darwin's chapters. Wallace asked Darwin, if he thought well of the essay, to send it on to Lyell.

It was one of those classic coincidences of science. Two men in different parts of the world had at the same moment independently arrived at the same startling new conclusions. For centuries life had been going on in all its abundance, its relationships were there for all to see, and yet until 1858 no one had made all the logical, enlightening connections. And then the answer had come not to one, but simultaneously to two men.

Even in the first instants of shock Darwin did not hesitate. He wrote at once to Lyell: "Your words have come true with a vengeance—that should be forestalled—I never saw a more striking coincidence. . . . So all my originality, whatever it may amount to, will be smashed, though my book, if it will ever have any value will not be deteriorated; as all the labour consists in the application of the theory."

Wallace had not mentioned publication, but Darwin said that he would "of course" write to him at once offering to send the essay to one of the journals. And in his letter to Lyell he added: "I hope you will approve of Wallace's sketch, that I may tell him what you say."

Hooker also was informed of what had happened. Darwin appealed to both friends for advice. He had not intended to publish his 1844 sketch, nor a letter he had recently written to Asa Gray, the American botanist, outlining the cardinal points in his theory. Could he honorably consider publishing them now because Wallace had sent him an outline of his doctrine?

"I would far rather burn my whole book than that he or any other man should think that I had behaved in a paltry spirit," Darwin wrote to Lyell, in what are surely some of the noblest, most unselfish words ever set down in a scientific controversy.

Hooker and Lyell went into urgent action. Hooker demanded that Darwin send him at once a copy of the 1844 sketch and of the letter to Gray. Darwin somehow got them off to him by a servant, but it was an automatic action. Scarlet fever, which had broken out the week before in the village, had spread to Down. On June 28 Darwin's youngest child, a defective eighteen-month-old baby, died of its ravages. Henrietta and two of the nurses were ill, showing some of the fearful symptoms. The other children had to be got out of the house to safety elsewhere. These were frantic hours.

Lyell and Hooker decided that a joint presentation of both Darwin's and Wallace's work was absolutely essential. Moving with the utmost rapidity, they laid the whole extraordinary problem before the Linnean Society—Darwin had so highly appreciated the importance of Wallace's work that he was proposing to publish it, a step of which Lyell and Hooker approved "provided he did not withhold from the public as he was strongly inclined to do (in favour of Mr. Wallace) the memoir which he himself had written on the same subject and which one of us had perused in 1844, and the contents of which we have both of us been privy to for many years." They said further that they were not considering claims to priority, but the interests of science generally. It was then arranged that relevant portions of both sketches should be read before the society's meeting of July 1.

Both Hooker and Lyell were present. As the meeting opened, they pleaded with the fellows to give the most careful consideration to the important subject they were about to hear—it was of the utmost significance.

As the secretary read the strange, world-shaking words of Wallace and Darwin, the Linnean Society members listened with suppressed excitement. But the reading was followed by silence; there was no discussion. "The subject was too novel and too ominous for the old school to enter the lists before armouring," Hooker wrote to Darwin the next day.

And with Hooker and Lyell standing guard, the "old school" did not dare without preparation to "fly out" against the disturbing theory they had just heard. The meeting had been called originally to hear a paper by George Bentham asserting the fixity of species. In the overawed hush, Bentham withdrew his work. He was not changing his position then, yet even in those first few moments he knew that the whole basis on which he had written was altered. He could no longer speak in the same terms. Few who were there realized that night that they would never again think wholly in the old terms or that the foundations of the world's thought in science and in every other field would be changed by the words the secretary had so dispassionately read.

Darwin was grateful; the joint reading was more than he could have hoped for. He had expected at the most that his material would be presented as an appendix to the Wallace essay. "I always thought it very possible that I might be forestalled," he wrote to Hooker with unsparing candor, "but I fancied that I had a grand enough soul not to care; but I found myself mistaken and punished. I had, however, resigned myself and had half written a letter to Wallace to give up all priority to him, and should certainly not have changed it if it had not been for Lyell's and your quite extraordinary kindness. . . . I am more than satisfied at what took place at the Linnean Society."

The panic at home also was relieved. Henrietta and one of the nurses who was believed to be developing scarlet fever had escaped. The other nurse was recovering. And the children were safe. The Darwins went off on a badly needed rest trip to the Isle of Wight, and there with a lighter heart Darwin began to prepare the abstract that all were agreed he must write at the first possible moment. It was to be a thirty-page article for the Linnean Society journal.

As he worked, the abstract grew in length. It could not be an article, it would have to be a book. John Murray, the publisher, agreed sight unseen at Lyell's behest to publish it. Although Darwin was again frequently "wretched" with headaches and "a very bad stomach," he managed in thirteen months of hard, unremitting work to finish his manuscript.

The title that Darwin had chosen, in recognition of the fact that this was not the full, definitive book he had so long planned, was *An Abstract of an Essay on the Origin of Species and Varieties through Natural Selection*. Murray said that it would have to be shortened. As the publisher read the alarming doctrine that Darwin was developing, he also became frightened. Murray, an amateur geologist, thought it "as absurd as though one could contemplate a fruitful union between a poker and a rabbit." He consulted the editor of the *Quarterly Review* and upon his advice proposed to Darwin that he drop his book and write instead a full account of his observations on pigeons, to which he might attach a brief summary of his general views with a promise of a later, larger work that would substantiate them in full. After all, Murray argued, "everybody is interested in pigeons."

Darwin yielded on the shortening of the title, but he flatly refused to scrap the book into which he had put his life. Murray gave in this time, and Darwin, "in an awful state of stomach" and "as weak as a child," struggled through the correction of proofs and all the other preliminaries of publication. One of the world's greatest and most influential books was not lost.

On November 24, 1859 the *Origin of Species* was published.

The twelve hundred and fifty copies Murray had printed for the first edition were sold to dealers on the first day, and a second edition of three thousand copies was ordered immediately.

In a world which still believed literally and fervently that all living animals were descended from those which

walked two by two into Noah's ark, and that the species
which had entered the ark had been created by God,
immutable and unchanging, the *Origin of Species* came
with a shattering shock.[3]

The *Quarterly Review* with quivering indignation
proclaimed that Darwin's theory "contradicted the revealed relation of the creation to its Creator," and was
"inconsistent with the fulness of His Glory." Darwin
was charged with using a collection of absurd facts "to
prop up his utterly rotten fabric of guess and speculation." Was it credible that all favorable varieties of tur-
nips were tending to become men? Who would dare to
talk of the "fruits and flowers" of plants of the carbonif-
erous epoch?

The *Athenaeum* with an undertone of derision attacked the "belief that man descends from monkeys."
Most scientists also disagreed positively with Darwin.
Even Lyell could not follow him to his ultimate conclusion that all life, if it included man, had descended from
one beginning.

In the overpowering wave of attack, *The Times* was
a signal exception. A remarkably unbiased article of
three and a half columns set forth the whole thesis of the
book clearly and simply, and the article concluded:
"The combined investigations of another twenty years

[3] Louis Agassiz expressed the typical opinion of the time
when he said: "The circumstance that species occur within
definite limits where no obstacles prevent their wider distribution leads to the further inference that these limits were as-
signed to them from the beginning, and so we should come to
the final conclusion that the order which prevails throughout
nature is intentional, that it is regulated by the limits marked
out on the first day of creation and that it has been maintained
unchanged through ages. . . ."

may, perhaps, enable naturalists to say whether the modifying causes and the selective power, which Mr. Darwin has satisfactorily shown to exist in Nature, are competent to produce all the effects he ascribes to them. . . ." Though the article was unsigned, Darwin at once suspected that Thomas H. Huxley was the writer; he was the only man in England with both the knowledge and the style to have written it. Of course Darwin was right. Huxley, a brilliant biologist, had long been dissatisfied with the miracle explanation of life's variety. As he read the *Origin* he found the better theory that he had been seeking; it was the flash of light in the dark, the working hypothesis science needed.

Huxley wrote to Darwin: "You have earned the lasting gratitude of all thoughtful men." And knowing the attacks that would come, he assured the beleaguered author: "As to the curs which will bark and yelp . . . you must recollect that some of your friends at any rate are endowed with an amount of combativeness that will stand you in good stead."

The gathering storm broke with fury at the meeting of the British Association for the Advancement of Science at Oxford late in June 1860.

The rumbling began at a meeting of Section D on Thursday, June 28. Two papers attacking Darwin were presented. Huxley, hoping to avoid a discussion at that point, kept silent after the first; but when the second speaker, Sir Richard Owen, declared that the brain of the gorilla differs from that of man more than from that of the lowest animal, Huxley fired back. He flatly denied Owen's statements and promised to produce more evidence later.

On Friday there was a lull. But on Saturday a meet-

ing had been scheduled at which John W. Draper, an
American and the President of New York University,
was to speak on "The Intellectual Development of
Europe, Considered with Reference to the Views of
Mr. Darwin and Others." Word went out that Samuel
Wilberforce, the Bishop of Oxford, also would take the
platform to "smash Darwin." An open clash between
the church and science seemed to be in the making.

Long before the meeting was to open, the room in
which it had been called was so overcrowded that a
shift had to be made to a larger room. It, in turn, was
soon crowded to suffocation with more than seven hundred men and women. Most of the ladies were sitting in
the long windows along the west side.

Draper droned on for more than an hour while the
crowd waited impatiently. When he finished, Henslow,
who was presiding, announced that only those who had
valid scientific arguments to present would be permitted
to address the meeting. Several who asked for the floor
received scant attention. When one man rushed to the
blackboard and scrawled two X's—"Let this Point A
be man, and that Point B be the monkey"—the undergraduates who were packed into one corner began to
yell "Monkey, monkey" until he was shouted down.

Henslow once more demanded only scientific arguments. At this the crowd began to call for the Bishop,
who had come in late. A professor of mathematics as
well as a cleric, he was thought to be especially well
qualified to deal with Darwin.

For half an hour the Bishop spoke, savagely ridicul-
ing Darwin and Huxley, and then he turned to Huxley,
who sat with him on the platform. In tones icy with

sarcasm he put his famous question: was it through his grandfather or his grandmother that he claimed descent from an ape?

The cheers rolled up and the ladies fluttered their white handkerchiefs. Henslow pounded for order. The Bishop had scored.

At the Bishop's question, Huxley had clapped the knee of the surprised scientist beside him and whispered: "The Lord hath delivered him into mine hands." The "wildcat" in Huxley was thoroughly aroused by what he considered the Bishop's insolence and ignorance, and he tore into the arguments Wilberforce had used. Huxley said later that as he listened to the Bishop's attack he made up his mind to "let him have it" and to let himself go. Working up to his climax, he shouted that he would feel no shame in having an ape as an ancestor, but that he would be ashamed of a brilliant man who plunged into scientific questions of which he knew nothing. In effect Huxley said that he would prefer an ape to the Bishop as an ancestor, and the crowd had no doubt of his meaning.[4]

The room dissolved into an uproar. Men jumped to their feet, shouting at this direct insult to the clergy. Lady Brewster fainted. Admiral Fitzroy, the former captain of the *Beagle*, waved a Bible aloft, shouting over the tumult that it, rather than the viper he had

---

[4] No one took down what was said. The only reports of this famous meeting have come from the later recollections of those who were present. Hooker told of his feelings in a letter written to Darwin the next day. Huxley described his own reactions in a letter to Sir Francis Darwin, written in 1891, and it confirmed previous reports of what he and the others had said.

harbored in his ship, was the true and unimpeachable authority. Arguments broke out all over the room, and Hooker said that his blood boiled.

"I never saw such a display of fierce party spirit," declared an anonymous writer in *MacMillan's Magazine*. "Looks of bitter hatred were directed to those who were on Darwin's side."

The issue had been joined. From that hour on, the quarrel over the elemental issue that the world believed was involved, science versus religion, was to rage unabated.

SEVEN

THE GREAT PRINCIPLE OF EVOLUTION

NO more mildly written book ever shook the world. The *Origin of Species* was a compilation of fact and un-argumentative argument; there were no denunciations of theories or individuals; scrupulous, deferential heed was given to contrary concepts, and there was no hint of an attack on religion. The whole tone was thoughtful, scientific, and modest to the point of abnegation. The explosive lay solely in the ideas expressed and in their inescapable implications. And it was to these ideas and implications that the world responded bitterly, rebel-liously, reluctantly, or jubilantly as the case might be.

As Julian Huxley, the grandson of Darwin's vigilant defender, pointed out, the *Origin's* case rested on three great facts and on two deductions that Darwin drew from them.

The first fact was the tendency of all living groups to increase in geometrical ratio; and the second, the tend-ency for the numbers of a given species to remain fairly constant. From these two facts Darwin drew his first deduction: there is a struggle for existence, a struggle that prevents geometric increase and holds down the numbers of any particular group. This led him to his third great fact: all living things involved in this gigantic struggle for life vary. And from this he reached his second deduction: the fittest are the ones that survive.

This powerful, almost irresistible argument was a unique combination of fact and reason, an interplay of induction and deduction, a remarkable progression from the particular to the general and from the part to the whole, from the individual to the universal.

The tendency toward geometric increase certainly was undeniable. There were no exceptions to it. Without checks, no district, no station, not even the whole surface of the earth could accommodate the progeny of a single pair after a certain number of generations.

Even slow-breeding man had doubled in twenty-five years in Darwin's own time, and it was simple for Darwin to calculate that if man continued to increase unchecked at his nineteenth-century rate his descendants literally would be without even standing-room on the earth in less than a thousand years. Linnaeus had pointed out that if an annual plant produced only two seeds—and there is no plant so unproductive—and if each of its seedlings produced only two, there would be a million plants in twenty years.

And that slowest breeder of all, the elephant, which seldom brings forth more than six young in its ninety years, would soon overrun the earth. Darwin estimated that in from seven hundred and forty to seven hundred and fifty years, nineteen million elephants would be trampling around the world.

Darwin, however, did not have to rely on theoretical calculations alone. With wonder and amazement he had seen such multiplication taking place. With his own hands he had dug the tooth of an extinct horse from the ground of the pampas, and as he did so, realized that the horse once had vanished completely from the Americas. From that time until the first European settlers came bringing their horses with them, there were none on the great plains of the Argentine. The enormous herds that roamed over the grassy pampas when Darwin visited the country in the 1830's all had sprung from a few immigrants. Darwin felt that if this increase had not been so well authenticated, even he could not have believed it. The horse had increased from zero to millions in a very few years.

He had seen too how a newcomer plant that had found halcyon conditions could sweep all before it.

No one could think that there had been any change in the fertility of the horse or the cardoon. The explanation, as Darwin understood, was that the conditions of life had been highly favorable; there was less destruction of the young and old, and unusual numbers of the young were able to breed. The geometric increase that Malthus had predicted was quickly under way.

"Lighten any check, mitigate the destruction ever so little, and the number of the species will almost instantaneously increase to any amount," said Darwin.

But even such an all-conquering invader as the prickly cardoon eventually came to a halt. And the ostrich, which laid a score of eggs, did not take over the world, nor did the English orchid whose 24,080 seeds Darwin counted by laying them on a long ruled line and whose great-grandchildren he figured could have clothed the entire surface of the globe with a uniform carpet of green. Except for the sudden runaways and spurts, the numbers of each species remained more or less constant over great periods of time. No one species or group—not man, not plants, not reptiles, not insects—had yet inherited the earth. The balance held.

From these two compelling facts Darwin drew his first deduction: there is a struggle for existence. "It inevitably follows from the high rate at which all organic beings tend to increase," he said. "It has truly been said that all nature is at war. . . ."

It was easy to admit this universal struggle for life; it was far more difficult, or at least Darwin explained that he found it so, to bear the fact constantly in mind. "Yet unless it be thoroughly engrained in the mind, the whole economy of nature with every fact on distribution, rarity, abundance, extinction, and variation will be dimly seen or quite misunderstood," Darwin warned. "We behold the face of nature bright with gladness . . . we do not see or we forget that the birds which are idly singing round us live on insects or seeds and are thus constantly destroying life; or we forget how largely these song-sters or their eggs or their nestlings are destroyed by birds and beasts of prey."

By a struggle for existence Darwin meant far more than a tooth-and-claw battle to the death. In the sense in which he used the term, a plant on the edge of the desert could be said to be in a struggle with the drought. A plant producing a thousand seeds of which only one came to maturity was, in this definition, in a struggle with other plants covering the ground and denying liv-ing-space to its progeny. Two mistletoes growing on the same branch and dependent for existence on dissemina-tion by the birds were competing with other fruit-bearing plants to tempt the birds to devour them and thus to spread their seeds.

Some experiments and observations in his own gar-den, "though on so infinitely a small scale," made the ever present but always elusive struggle very real for Darwin. One spring he measured off a two-by-three-foot piece of ground and had it dug up and cleared. Every day on his walks he stopped by to mark each seedling that came up. By the end of the season three hundred and fifty-seven seedlings had pushed their heads above the ground, and though there was no choking from other plants in the little plot, two hundred and ninety-five of them were destroyed, principally by slugs and insects. The weeds' struggle for existence was a severe one; eightly-three per cent perished.

Darwin also sowed fifteen kinds of seeds in his meadow, where the young plants had to make their way against the competition of the plants already established there. Fifteen of the seeds germinated, but they died so rapidly that not one succeeded in flowering.

Darwin had another firsthand experience with the inexorability of the struggle and the delicacy of its balance. In Surrey, not far from Down, was an ancient heath where cattle had browsed through time immemorial. Marking off one of its boundaries were some low hills on which grew a few clumps of Scotch fir.

But times changed and over a period of ten years large parts of the heath were fenced to exclude the cattle. Walking over this enclosed part of the heath, Darwin was amazed to discover that millions of young Scotch firs were springing up. They were so nearly of the same size he checked to see if they could possibly have been planted.

And yet as he looked out toward the open heath, Darwin could not see a single fir. He climbed to a vantage point where he could have a better view, and still not one was in sight. Darwin went down to the open part of the heath and began to examine it closely. When he pushed the stems aside he discovered that hidden among them was a multitude of seedlings and little fir trees cropped down by the cattle. In one square yard

he counted thirty-two tiny trees, no one of which had
ever succeeded in raising its head above the level of the
heath covering. One, no thicker "than a stick of sealing
wax," showed twenty-six rings of annual growth; the
cattle had kept it down for a quarter of a century. It was
no longer a mystery to Darwin why the firs sprang up
by the million as soon as the cattle were excluded. The
cattle absolutely determined the existence of the trees.

"What a play of forces, determining the kind and
proportion of each plant in a square yard of turf!" wrote
Darwin. "It is to my mind truly wonderful. And yet
we are pleased to wonder when some animal or plant
becomes extinct . . . and as we do not see the cause
we invoke cataclysms to desolate the world."

Sometimes, however, it was animals and plants remote in the scale of nature that were bound together in a
complex web of life and death. In his meadow Darwin
covered one hundred heads of red clover, thus barring
the visits of bees. They produced not a single seed,
though one hundred near-by heads of clover around
which the bees had swarmed matured twenty-seven hundred seeds. Darwin saw that only the bumblebee visited
the red clover; only this bee was able to reach its nectar.

And Darwin carried the story on, one of the classic
stories of science. The number of bumblebees in any district depended on the number of field mice, for the mice
destroyed the bees' nests and combs. And the number of
field mice depended on the number of cats in adjacent
villages. "Hence," Darwin said, "it is quite credible that
the presence of a feline animal in large numbers in a
district might determine through the intervention first of
mice and then of bees, the frequency of certain flowers
in that district."

Battle within battle was continuously recurring. The struggle was most severe, though, between individuals of the same species living in the same district, eating the same foods and exposed to the same dangers. Thus in Scotland an increase in the missel thrush caused a decrease in the song thrush. In Russia the small Asiatic cockroach drove out the big Russian species. In Australia the imported hive bee quickly supplanted the native bee.

In no one case perhaps was it possible to say precisely why one species was victorious and another the loser in the no-quarter battle for life. But, thinking about this intricate problem, Darwin could not escape the conviction, he said, that the structure of every organic being is related in the most essential yet often hidden manner to that of all the other organic beings with which it comes into competition for food or living-space, or from which it has to escape or on which it preys. All were inextricably linked, the possessor and the competitor, the attacker and the attacked, the predator and the hunted.

The full picture of the great web of life might well be beyond man's discovery and comprehension. All we can do, said Darwin, "is to keep steady in mind that each organic being is striving to increase in a geometrical ratio; that each at some period of its life, during some season of the year, has to struggle for life, and to suffer great destruction."

Darwin's third fact—that all living things vary—underlay his theory. Few could doubt it, for every human being has to be aware that he himself is different from all others, and that all the living things around him vary.[1]

[1] The one exception among sexually produced beings is identical twins.

To a scientist comparing closely, the differences were even more marked. To Darwin, laboring over his barnacles, comparing organ with organ, it was evident that every part of every individual was different from all others.

Many of these individual differences—the brown eyes, the notched edge of the leaf, the stripes of the tiger—were inherited. But how was not clear. Darwin was forced time and again to say "the laws governing inheritance are for the most part unknown," and "we are profoundly ignorant of why this or that part has varied."

Ironically, at the very time the English naturalist was struggling with this perplexing problem, an Austrian monk, of whose work Darwin knew nothing, was solving it. Abbot Gregor Mendel, in his little strip of garden beneath the white walls of the Augustinian monastery of Brünn, had learned by crossing peas that traits are passed along from parent to offspring by precise mathematical combinations and recombinations of hereditary units that ultimately were to be called genes. His work laid the basis for the science of genetics. Mendel's enlightening findings were published in 1866, only six years after the *Origin of Species* had appeared, and while Darwin was in the midst of studies dealing with heredity. It lay unnoticed, however, in a few scattered libraries, and the world at large knew nothing of it until it was suddenly rediscovered in 1900 by three scientists, each working independently.

Darwin too had worked with peas. Like Mendel, he saw that if he crossed green and yellow peas, all of those in the next generation were yellow, and that when two of the hybrids were crossed, some of the peas "reverted" to the green of the grandparents. But Darwin, unlike

Mendel, was not a mathematician. The significance of the combinations that he saw escaped him.

"Can we doubt (remembering that many more individuals are born than can possibly survive) that individuals having any advantage, however slight over others would have the best chance of surviving and of procreating their kind?" asked Darwin. "On the other hand, we may feel sure that any variation in the least degree injurious would be rigidly destroyed."

In these two sentences Darwin summed up his second major deduction. He called the principle natural selection, or later, borrowing a term from Herbert Spencer, the survival of the fittest. In much the same way that Newton's discovery of the law of gravity explained a vast array of natural phenomena, so did natural selection suddenly explain an endless number of formerly unrelated, baffling, and unreachable facts of nature.

It provided at once a new answer to that eternal question: why do some live rather than others? If all individuals of every species were exactly alike, survival would be a matter of chance. But all were not alike. Some were stronger, some swifter, some hardier, and some more cunning. The green of one leaf-eater more perfectly matched that of the leaf; the mottled gray of one bark-eater came closer to that of the bark; the white of one ptarmigan was exactly that of the winter snow; and these were the individuals most likely to survive and leave descendants. Among the plants the smallest differences must have weighed the balance. Perhaps the earliest shoot escaped the slug, or the most vigorous flowered first in an early autumn, or the one best armed with hairs and spines was not devoured, or the most conspicuous was the one fertilized. As Wallace aptly stated it, "any beneficial variation will give the possessor of it a greater probability of living through the tremendous ordeal that all have to undergo. There may be something left to chance, but on the whole the fittest survive." And as this process was repeated over and over again through age after age, all living things came to be beautifully and successfully adapted to the environment in which they live and to the web of life in which they move.

To trace more explicitly how this evident but nearly incomprehensible result might have come to pass, Darwin proposed a hypothetical case. Suppose, he said, that all bumblebees were somehow to be eliminated from a certain field where red clover grew. As the red clover depends on the bumblebee for pollination, it would be doomed, unless— But perhaps among all the blossoms in the field there might be one whose corolla was just the fraction shorter that would make it possible for the ordinary hive bee to suck its nectar. It would be the only clover that could survive. And because its descendants in all probability also would have a short corolla, a new relationship between bee and clover would be established. A slightly different red clover would take over the field. Or perhaps among all the hive bees in the field there might be one with a proboscis long enough or differently enough constructed to reach the flowers of the usual red clover. That bee, having found a new and abundant supply of nectar, would have a rare advantage over its fellow bees and in all likelihood would soon outnumber them.

"Thus I can understand," said Darwin, "how a flower and a bee might slowly become either simultaneously or one after the other modified and adapted to each other

in the most perfect manner, by the continued preservation of all individuals which presented slight deviations
of structure mutually favourable to each other."

It might be the one adaptation or the other that would
prevail; Darwin saw that there was no predetermined
way even to the same end. The proof was everywhere.
How differently constructed were the feathered wing of
a bird and the membrane-covered wing of a bat, the four
wings of a butterfly and the two wings and elytra of the
beetle! Darwin had been fascinated too by the different
hinges the bivalves had developed for opening and
shutting their shells. They ranged from the long row of
neatly interlocking teeth of the *Nucula* to the simple liga-
ment of the mussel. Seeds, he pointed out, were dis-
seminated by their minuteness, by converting their capsules into balloon-like envelopes, by being embedded in
pulp, by being nutritious or conspicuously colored so as
to attract and be devoured by the birds, by having hooks
or grapnels for clinging to the fur of animals, or by being
furnished with wings and plumes as different in shape
as they were perfectly formed for floating in even the
lightest breeze.

By natural selection such adaptions might be carried
to almost unbelievable perfection, as they had been in
the orchid. The "contrivances" by which the pollen of
the orchid is transferred from one plant to another are as
varied and "almost as perfect as the most beautiful adaptations in the animal kingdom," Darwin noted.

A favorite walk of Darwin's was to orchis bank, a spot
near Down where many varieties of English orchids
grew. Later, as he pressed on into his speculations on
the origin of species, Darwin became convinced that
cross-fertilization plays an important part in keeping

species constant, and this led him to expand his work on orchids, for they were an unsurpassed example of the cross-fertilization of flowers by insects. In 1862 he published his book *The Fertilisation of Orchids*. It was another classic, a book so clear and so accurate that no one since, no expert with all the facilities of modern science, has been able to change its observations or conclusions.

A collector in Madagascar sent Darwin one of the beautiful Star of Bethlehem orchids that grow there. Its six-rayed flowers were like stars of snow-white wax, and from them depended an extraordinary long green-white nectary. When he measured the nectar tube, Darwin discovered with amazement that it was eleven and a half inches in length and that only the lower inch and and a half was filled with nectar. He ventured to suggest that there must be an insect with a proboscis long enough to reach it. Entomologists replied with ridicule; no such insect existed.

Darwin patiently worked on. He took a cylindrical rod a tenth of an inch in diameter and pushed it down through the orchid into the long nectary. As he withdrew it, a viscid strip of membrane on either side of the cleft rostellum firmly adhered to it and the pollen masses were withdrawn on the rod. Darwin tried his experiment again. Again the rod came out with the pollen masses attached. If some huge moth had inserted its proboscis into the flower, the pollen masses would have been glued to it just as they were to Darwin's rod, and the moth would have carried them away to pollinate another flower. Unless there was a moth with a ten- or eleven-inch proboscis, Darwin did not see how the Star of Bethlehem could have survived. Without cross-fertilization the orchid would have become extinct.

Some time later the moth that Darwin had envisioned was found. Its coiled proboscis could be unrolled to reach the Star of Bethlehem's nectar. Darwin's reasoning and his understanding of the function of each part of this lovely, fragile orchid had been unerring.

The *Coryanthes*, or bucket orchid, was another example of the almost incredible adaptation of insects and flower. No man, Darwin thought, could ever have guessed, if he had not seen, the use to which each part of this orchid was put. The lower lip of the *Coryanthes* forms a large bucket, which is kept half filled with water dropped from two secreting horns just above it. In another small chamber just above the bucket are two curious fleshy ridges.

Crowds of bumblebees visit the orchid to gnaw the ridges. In their competition for the delicacy some of the bees always are pushed off and fall into the bucket. With their wings wet by the water they cannot fly away; they must try to crawl out of their involuntary bath. As they soon learn, there is only one way out. Three sides of the bucket are slippery, waxy and steep, but on the other are some ridges which in effect are a "bee staircase." Climbing up, the bee is forced to enter a flowery passage in which it rubs against the orchid's sticky pollen masses. They are nicely glued to its back. No sooner does the bee crawl out of the orchid than it looks for another fleshy ridge on which to feast. Before long it falls into the bucket again and in crawling out the same way inserts the pollen masses into the stigma and thus pollinates either the same or another flower. A procession of bees can often be seen crawling in and out of a *Coryanthes*.

A botanist friend sent Darwin one of the orchids which had been preserved in "spirits of wine." In it was a bee that he had killed just as it was crawling out with one of the pollen masses fastened, like a miniature knob, to its back.

And natural selection had fashioned the still more remarkable *Catasetum* orchid. A bee visiting this leopard-spotted orchid seldom can avoid touching a long prong-like flower "trigger." The touch ruptures a membrane and this sets free a spring whose recoil shoots forth a pollen mass, almost as an arrow is shot from a bow. The blunt-tipped pollinium flies out in exactly the right way to hit the invading bee on the back. Adhesive material on its end firmly fastens it to its landing-place.

Sooner or later the pollen-carrying bee flies to a female *Catasetum*—only the male flower has the firing apparatus. It is brought in contact there with a stigma sticky enough to strip the pollen mass from its back, and the purpose for which centuries of adaptation have fashioned this strange flower catapult is achieved.

Darwin held one of the orchids about a yard from his study window and lightly touched the trigger prong. The pollinium hit the pane of glass and stuck by its adhesive disc to the smooth vertical surface.[2] Darwin marveled. To see the plant "fire" was an unforgettable experience. By dissecting the orchid he laid bare the whole apparatus, and yet it seemed impossible that it could act as it did. Would a mechanical device work on the same principle?

Darwin took a tiny strip of whalebone and slightly weighted it at one end to represent the disc-projectile. He bent it halfway around a small cylinder, gently holding the upper end with the smooth head of a pin. At this

   [2] Other orchid experts have seen the pollen mass fly out for a distance of six feet—in fact have been hit by it at that distance.

point he let go of the other end. The whalebone was pitched forward exactly like the pollinium and with its weighted end foremost!

"The more I study Nature," Darwin said, "the more I become impressed . . . that the contrivances and beautiful adaptations slowly acquired through each part occasionally varying in a slight degree, but in many ways, with the preservation of those variations which were beneficial to the organism under complex varying conditions of life, transcend in an incomparable manner the contrivances and adaptations which the most fertile imagination of man could invent."

Darwin's theory of natural selection and his deep feeling about it were encompassed in this long, difficult sentence. When he started a sentence he felt compelled to include all the circumstances that might affect the meaning of what he wanted to say. This weighing of all facts, large and small, was part of his approach to science.

It was also the piling up, the accumulation of differences, that had over a great period of time produced new species. Acceptance of this thesis, however, only raised a myriad of new problems. How could the lesser differences between individuals and varieties become augmented into the wider differences between species, differences so broad that there could seldom be interbreeding?

As he always did, Darwin began to seek his answer in the tangible. How had domestic animals become different? At an earlier period, he knew, the Arabs had required swift horses; the people of northern Europe had wanted stronger, bulkier ones. At first the differences in the horses were small, but as the one group continually selected for speed and the other for strength, two sub-breeds were created. As the differences between the two breeds became more marked, animals that were neither particularly fleet nor particularly strong were not used for breeding. The intermediates disappeared. Thus through man's actions differences that were at first only perceptible were increased until the two breeds diverged in character. Looking at the sleek, speedy Arabian and the heavy, stanch Percheron, it was easy to forget that both had descended from a common ancestor.

But the problem Darwin had faced before on natural selection arose to confront him again. What could produce the same kind of divergence in nature? For years he worried over this puzzle, and then one day as he was out driving in his carriage the solution suddenly came to him. He always remembered the exact spot in the road, he said in his autobiography.

The answer was essentially a simple one. The more diversified the descendants of any one species became in structure, constitution, and habits, the better they would be able to seize on widely diversified places in nature, and the more they could increase. The mammals that could fly and those that could swim or climb trees found new opportunities; they flourished and increased. In nature it paid to be different, and thus the large groups fanned out in many different ways.

"It is a truly wonderful fact—the wonder of which we are apt to overlook from familiarity—that all animals and all plants throughout all time and space should be related to each other in groups," Darwin wrote in the *Origin*.

As living things increased and could occupy new environments and new stations, they spread around the world. Where there were no impassable barriers, life inched onward. But in many places there were barriers, the greatest being, of course, the oceans. How, Darwin asked, could animals that could not swim or fly reach continents separated by broad oceans, or oceanic islands entirely surrounded by water? When it was assumed that each species had been separately created, no such problem existed, for it was believed that God could place his creations where He willed. Darwin, however, resting his case on the descent of all living species from common ancestors, was compelled thereby to explain how they could have reached some of the isolated places they occupied. If all life had spread from one center or a few centers, he had to show how it had spread. The question of geographic distribution was a crucial one to the writer of the *Origin of Species*.

"No subject gives me so much trouble and doubt and difficulty as the means of dispersal of the same species of terrestrial productions on the oceanic islands," Darwin wrote to his cousin William Darwin Fox.

If Darwin had been willing to accept the continental theories of some of the leading geologists of the day, his task would have been far easier. They were insisting in the late 1850's and 1860's that the land and water had interchanged position so frequently within the time of life that connections might well have existed between all the continents and islands. In a half-playful, half-rueful letter to Hooker, Darwin complained that some of the geologists were taking the position that you could make continents as easily as a cook does pancakes. Darwin, on the other hand, was convinced by all that he had seen that the continents as continents and the oceans as oceans were of immense antiquity, and that they had held these positions—though with many lesser changes —long before the existence of recent species.

But if there had never been a land bridge to the Galápagos and other oceanic islands, how had non-swimming, non-flying reptiles, insects, and plants reached their shores? Could seeds have floated there? Hooker, the botanical authority, did not think that seeds would grow after so long an immersion in salt water. Darwin determined to find out.

He put some cress, radish, carrot, onion, and celery seeds in bottles of salt water. Some of the bottles he dropped into a big tank of water that he cooled to thirty-two or thirty-three degrees with snow. After a week the water in the bottles "smelt very badly" and the seeds had emitted such a wonderful quantity of mucus that Darwin said he half expected them to turn into tadpole. But when he planted the seeds, they germinated and grew "splendidly." He next tried a fourteen-day immersion, and then one of twenty-one days.

"Will you beat Dr. Hooker?" asked the children as they watched the experiments.

Darwin did. After twenty-one days the cress and lettuce seed still germinated. In the end, Darwin found that sixty-four out of eighty-seven kinds of seed would germinate after an immersion of twenty-eight days; a few survived one hundred and thirty-seven days of immersion.

In a sea current moving a mile an hour, seeds could be transported one hundred and sixty-eight miles in a week, and the Gulf Stream, some of Darwin's data said, flowed fifty to sixty miles a day. Darwin felt that he was beginning to find the seeds' mode of travel. At this point, however, Hooker asked how he could be sure that the seeds would float; they might well sink.

As Darwin watched, many of his small seeds went to the bottom of the tank, and his heart sank as well. It looked as though he had taken all his trouble in "salting the ungrateful rascals" for nothing. And yet at the Keeling Islands he had been told that many seeds washed ashore. He decided to try some larger fruit and seed capsules, and they obligingly floated for a long time. And so did dried branches bearing fruits or seeds. The seeds of one asparagus plant grew after it had floated for eighty-five days.

Perhaps too there were other ways in which seeds could reach remote islands. Darwin fed some soaked seeds to fish at the Zoological Society. As he stood before their tank watching, he was imagining that the fish had been swallowed by a heron and that the seeds had been voided on the shore of some distant lake and had germinated beautifully when "lo and behold the fish ejected vehemently, with a disgust equal to my own, all the seeds from their mouths."

Later the experiment succeeded. Darwin found that the fish would greedily eat the seeds of aquatic grasses. He fed some of his grass-fed fish to a stork, and when the seeds were voided, they germinated.

Perhaps too seeds were carried to the oceanic islands by driftwood. When stones are embedded in the roots of trees, bits of earth also are frequently enclosed, so tightly that not a particle would be washed away in the longest transport in the sea. Out of one small portion of earth enclosed by the roots of a fifty-year-old oak Darwin obtained three dicotyledonous plants that germinated well in his hothouse.

It seemed to Darwin too that living birds, which often are blown great distances across the sea, must carry seeds to the islands. He established to his own satisfaction that seeds are not injured by passage through the intestines of birds. He fed some seeds to the hawks at the Zoological Society. Twelve to twenty hours later, he reported to Hooker, the hawks "behaved like gentlemen" and cast up pellets with a lot of the seeds in them. When the seeds were planted, they grew.

Seeds might also be transported on the mud-caked feet of birds. A friend sent Darwin the leg of a woodcock to which a tiny pellet of earth adhered. Although it weighed only nine grains, in it was the seed of a toad rush that not only germinated, but flowered in Darwin's garden. Darwin also obtained a ball of earth from the leg of a red-legged partridge. The earth had been kept for three years, but when Darwin watered it and placed it under a bell glass, no fewer than eighty-two plants sprang from it.

"I think it would be a marvellous fact if many plants had not been transported," Darwin concluded.

Far more difficult to figure out was the route of travel used by fresh-water mollusks, the shells that are distributed so widely in the world's fresh waters. If he was correct in thinking that all shells had descended from a common stock, Darwin had to explain how the mollusks could get from one body of fresh water to another separated from it by hundreds of miles of sea. Floating was out of the question, for their ova are killed quickly by salt water, and it was unlikely that they would be carried by birds or fish. Writing to Hooker, as he always did about any problem that perplexed him, Darwin complained that the shells were driving him wild and were a "horrid incubus." He was completely baffled until he happened to notice one day that some ducks coming out of a pond were covered with duckweed. Ducks' duck-weed! Darwin's ingenious mind had its clue. He had often noticed that when he moved duckweed from one aquarium to another he often unintentionally stocked one aquarium with fresh-water shells from another. He scarcely could wait, he said, to try out the idea that had flashed into his mind.

Darwin dangled the feet of a duck in his aquarium at a time when many ova of fresh-water shells were hatching. Thirty or forty of the extremely minute just-hatched shells climbed on the duck's feet and could not be jarred or jerked off. There they survived, out of water, for twenty to twenty-four hours. In that time a duck could fly at least six hundred to seven hundred miles, and if blown across the sea to an oceanic island, it would be sure to alight on a pond or rivulet. Darwin had discovered the mollusk route of travel.

The animals that had not reached the islands were equally revealing. Darwin could think of no way in which the soft, slimy spawn of frogs could be trans-ported across great stretches of salt water, and signifi-cantly there were no frogs on the islands. Nor could Darwin map out any way, short of a land bridge, that non-swimming, non-flying mammals might take to a distant island. And again, significantly there were no mammals on the oceanic islands.

One by one, perhaps, the eggs and the seeds had ar-rived from distant continents, washing in on the waves, drifting in on an uprooted tree or a dried stalk, or planing in to the islands on the feet or in the bodies of birds. And only those which could survive such modes

of transportation had come. The life of the oceanic islands was no longer an obstacle to Darwin's theory; it
was, on the contrary, a strong and unexpected confirma-
tion of it.

In writing the *Origin* Darwin had been able to use
only a fraction of the materials stored in the big portfolios on his carefully labeled shelves. "I'm a complete
millionaire in odd and curious little facts," he once told
a friend. It had worried him that readers of the *Origin*
had been forced to take some of his statements on trust,
without seeing his substantiating evidence.

Soon after the publication of his book on orchids,
Darwin began to bring together his vast accumulation
on variations in animals and plants under domestication.
Working on the book he planned on this subject was
wearing, for his health continued bad. Reading made his
head "whiz" more than ever, and his diary for 1864
bears the typical note: "Ill all January, February, and
March." During the decade 1860 to 1870, Henrietta
also was seriously ill and the family went through another bout with scarlet fever as well as many lesser ill-
nesses. After the Huxleys had lost a child, Emma begged
Mrs. Huxley to come to Down for a rest, bringing the
three children then at home and a nurse. Mrs. Huxley
expressed her gratitude but explained that she was too
weak and ill to leave her room before afternoon. Emma
immediately replied that this was the usual state of the
family at Down and that the Huxleys would only be
following suit. At Down, as Gwen Raverat saw it, it
was a "distinction and a mournful pleasure to be ill."
This she thought was partly because Darwin always was

ill and the children adored him and were inclined to imitate him, and partly because it was so "delightful to be pitied and nursed" by Emma.[3]

William, the oldest son, had gone to Cambridge in 1858. Quite a bit of money had been spent on papering and fixing up his rooms when he decided that they were noisy and that he would like to move into the rooms his father had occupied in his student days. In an affectionate letter Darwin told him to make the change if he wished. And then he continued: "I do hope that you will keep up your already acquired energetic and industrious habits; your success in life will largely depend on this. So much for preachment, but it is a good old established custom that he who pays may preach; and as I shall have to pay if you move (as I rather advise) so I have had my preach."

This very gentle preachment with its drawing back and softening of anything that could be considered even slight criticism was as far as Darwin ever went in directing his children. It was in striking contrast to his father's imperious manner to him.

William could remember only one occasion when his father had spoken to him in anger. On returning from a meeting he made some flippant remark about a governor of Jamaica who was on trial for the use of brutality in suppressing a rebellion of Negroes. Darwin turned on his son in a burst of anger and told him that he had better go back to Southampton—where the meet-

[3] When Henrietta was recuperating from an illness at the age of thirteen, the doctor recommended that she have breakfast in bed. Mrs. Raverat is responsible for the statement that she never got up for breakfast again in the eighty-six years of her life.

ing had been held. The next morning at seven o'clock he came to William's bedside to say how sorry he was that he had been angry. He had not slept, worrying about what he considered his outburst.

Darwin was incapable of wounding the feelings of another human, and he had a sixth sense as to where sensitive spots might lie. In a day when servants were often ordered about, Darwin never made the simplest request without a "will you be so kind as to" or some other preface of the kind.

And this consideration did not extend only to those around him. Anyone who wrote Darwin was answered with the most exquisite courtesy and respect. When the volume of his correspondence became overwhelming, he had a form letter prepared, but seldom could bring himself to use it.

His reply to John Scott, who sent him a manuscript with a request for criticism, was typical of his handling of any serious matter:

I have read your paper with much interest. Shall you think me impertinent (I am sure I do not mean to be so) if I hazard a remark on the style, which is of more importance than many think? In my opinion (whether or not worth much), your paper would have been much better if written more simply and less elaborated—more like your letters. It is a golden rule always to use, if possible, a short old Saxon word. Such a sentence as "So purely dependent is the incipient plant on the specific morphological tendency" does not sound to my ears like good mother-English—it wants translating. Here and there you might, I think, have condensed some sentences. I go on the plan of thinking that every single word which can be omitted without actual loss of sense is a decided gain. Now perhaps

you will think me a meddling intruder: anyhow it is the
advice of an old hackneyed writer who sincerely wishes
you well.

Brutality, particularly to the helpless, was literally un-
bearable to Darwin. All his life he passionately hated
slavery, and it was this irrepressible feeling that pro-
voked one of the few quarrels he had with Captain Fitzroy during the voyage of the *Beagle*. In Brazil, Fitzroy
had gone to visit the estate of a large slave-owner and
returned glowing with approval of its efficiency and the
kindness with which the slaves were treated. The owner
had asked several of them in Fitzroy's presence if they
wished to be free. Their answer had been no. Darwin
could not endure this; he coldly asked the Captain what
he thought the answer of a slave was worth in the presence of his master. Fitzroy was furious; he ordered
Darwin to get out, and Charles thought at first that he
would have to leave the ship. A few hours later, however, the Captain had calmed down and sent an officer
with his apologies and a request that Mr. Darwin continue to dine with him.

Feeling as he did about slavery, Darwin was more
engrossed during the 1860's with the Civil War than
with the relatively quiet political affairs in England. He
read Olmstead's *Journey in the Slave States* and could
not, he said, keep his mind away from some of the inci-
dents reported. They caused him many another sleepless
night.

In 1861 he wrote to Hooker: "I never knew the
newspapers so profoundly interesting. North America
does not do England justice; I have not seen or heard of
a soul who is not with the North. . . . Some few, and

I am one of them, even wish to God, though at a loss of millions of lives, that the North would proclaim a crusade against slavery. . . . What wonderful times we live in! Massachusetts seems to show noble enthusiasm. Great God! How I should like to see the greatest curse on earth—slavery—abolished!"

Letters to Asa Gray, who was then ardently defending the *Origin* in the United States and bringing about its American publication, also emphasized his live sympathy with the North.

Darwin's health mended a bit toward the middle of the decade, and it was a notable event in the family that he attended a soiree given by the Royal Society. He met many of his old friends, some of whom he had not seen for many years, and most of whom failed to recognize him. Time had brought changes, of course, for Darwin had become quite bald, but it was the long, full beard that he had grown that changed him almost unrecognizably. The president of the society presented Darwin and two other guests to the Prince of Wales. The prince murmured something that Darwin could not catch, so, as Emma reported, "Charles made his profoundest bow and went on."

In the summer of 1868 the Darwins took a house on the Isle of Wight for six weeks. Tennyson, who was living near by, soon came to call. At first the Darwins were not overly impressed by their famous neighbor, but gradually, Emma said, they came to like him and his "absurd talk." During this visit to the Isle of Wight the Darwins also met Longfellow and his brother-in-law Tom Appleton. The two were full of the wonders of "table-turning, spirits and ghosts" and did their best to interest Darwin in the craze of the hour. They had half convinced Tennyson by taking him into an orchard at night to hear their weird stories by lantern light.

The two volumes on *Animals and Plants under Domestication* had been published on January 30, 1868. Darwin, finishing the four years of work that went into the two large books, had felt weary and discouraged about them—they were not worth a fifth of the enormous labor they had taken, and the devil take the whole thing! Ten days later, though, when word came from Murray that the fifteen hundred copies of the first edition had sold out in a week and a favorable review had appeared in the *Pall Mall*, it did Darwin "a world of good." "I'm quite content," he wrote Hooker, "and do not care how much I may be pitched into."

At the outset of his work on species, Darwin saw that if he could demonstrate how domestic cattle, horses, dogs, cats, pigeons, grains, flowers, and fruits had developed from earlier, different ancestors, he could cut part of the ground out from under those who maintained that species could not have changed. The opportunity lay clear before him, but it involved enormous work.

Year after year Darwin delved into history, ancient literature, art, breeders' records, and comparative anatomy, and carried on extensive experiments of his own: everything to trace the modern breeds back to their ancestors. This took the most rugged kind of pioneering; no one before him had attempted anything of the kind.

Darwin carried the dog back to several wolf-like ancestors, horses to a dun-colored wild ancestor, the peach to a modified almond, wheat to a small grained plant, and the game fowls to a wild bird called *Gallus bankiva* that had originally lived at the base of the

Himalayas. But he gave his closest attention to the pigeon. Of all the domesticated animals, its ancestry could be traced most fully. The chesty pouter, the sleek long-necked carrier, the showy fantail, and all the others of the hundred and fifty modern species went back to the bluish rock pigeon that once had nested among the bleak rocks on Asiatic shores. The modern forms differed so radically both from their ancestors and from each other that Darwin said he scarcely could persuade himself that all of them had arisen since man first domesticated the rock pigeon perhaps five thousand years earlier.

Some of the modifications had appeared since 1600, when Abker Khan of India had carried twenty thousand pigeons around with his court and had improved some of his breeds by crossing them with rare varieties sent to him by the monarch of Iran and Turan. Abker's turbit had no frill, his pouter waddled around on shorter legs, his fantail displayed fewer feathers, and the beaks and wattles of his carriers were far less developed than those of the pigeons Darwin was breeding.

It was particularly significant that the differences among Abker's pigeons were much less pronounced than those among modern pigeons. In short, Darwin discovered with great pleasure, the breeds in 1600 had not diverged as much from their common parent, the rock pigeon, as had their descendants. His theory of divergence was well supported.

Early in his pigeon work Darwin had set up an aviary of his own in an old summerhouse shaded by a walnut tree. He also joined two societies of pigeon-fanciers, and the latter he soon found were a distinctive breed in themselves.

One night Darwin went up to London to attend a

meeting of the Columbarian Society. It was held in a London "gin palace," and as soon as dinner was finished a Mr. Brent, "a queer little fish," handed Darwin a clay pipe. It was taken for granted that he would smoke. As the squire—their name for Darwin—and the fanciers solemnly sat around the table surrounded by clouds of smoke, it was hinted that Mr. Bull had crossed his pouters with runts to gain size. To Darwin's secret amusement, solemn shakes of the head greeted news of this scandalous proceeding, for, completely ignoring the pigeon's history, the fanciers deplored cross-breeding. The squire nevertheless nodded in true agreement when one member concluded: "If it was possible for noblemen and gentlemen to know the amazing amount of solace and pleasure derived from the almond tumbler, scarcely any nobleman or gentleman would be without their aviaries." Darwin remembered how he had once wondered why all gentlemen did not become ornithologists, and he wrote to his son William that pigeon-raising was "a majestic and noble pursuit that beats moths and butterflies, whatever you say to the contrary."

Darwin's pigeons and his animals, fruits, and flowers piled up almost incontrovertible evidence that new domesticated breeds had been created by man. And yet Darwin with all of his careful research was not able to discover all the intermediate forms; many links were missing, though all the changes had occurred within the history of man. Why, then, Darwin asked his doubters, should it be denied that other living things had changed and that new species had evolved? Or why should there be surprise that in nature many links were missing?

EIGHT

THE HIGHEST PROBLEM—MAN

THE QUESTION of questions still had to be fully faced.[1]

As early as 1837, when he opened his first notebook on species, Darwin "could not avoid" the belief that man came under the same law as all other living things; that he too had descended from the same ancestors and ultimately from that first living filament of which his grandfather had spoken. Darwin collected notes on the subject of man, for his own satisfaction, he said, and without any intention of publishing.

When he was working on the *Origin*, Wallace once asked him if he thought he would discuss man. Darwin answered that he thought he would avoid the whole subject "as so surrounded with prejudices," though he was ready to admit that it was the highest and most interesting problem for the naturalist. He also felt that it would be "useless and injurious" to go into man's derivation without giving all the evidence in full, and that, of course, he was unable to do in the tight confines of the *Origin*.

And yet with that conscientious honesty of his, Darwin did not want to conceal his views. In order that no "honourable man" should accuse him of deception, he added a brief statement to the *Origin*. He said that by

[1] "The question of questions for mankind—the problem which underlies all others and is more deeply interesting than any other—is the ascertainment of the place which Man occupies in nature and his relations to the universe of things"— T. H. Huxley: *Man's Place in Nature* (New York: D. Appleton & Company; 1892).

the work "light would be thrown on the origin of man and his history." That was all there was to it.

It was more than enough to arouse the furor he had dreaded. Many of the critics dived straight for the point. Five days after publication the *Athenaeum* charged that the "belief that man descends from the monkeys" had been wrought by Darwin into something like a creed. Sedgwick, Darwin's college professor of geology, wrote Darwin in combined sorrow and anger, expressing his gravest fears that the theory set forth in the *Origin* would "brutalize humanity" and "sink it into a lower grade of degradation than any into which it has fallen since its written records tell us of its history." Relenting a little, he signed himself "a son of a monkey and an old friend of yours." The ape, of course, formed the climax of the attack the Bishop of Oxford made on Huxley.

Darwin met the charge with dignity and patience. He did not fight back. Sedgwick could not possibly have paid him a "more honourable compliment than in freely expressing his disapprobation," and he was grieved to have shocked a man he had so long held in high respect. And surely Sedgwick would agree that "truth can only be known by rising victorious from every attack."

Although the issue of man and his origins was twisted and misinterpreted, it was at last out in the open. There was no longer much reason to avoid it. Darwin began to think a few years after the *Origin's* publication that the subject of man should be thoroughly discussed by a scientist who shared his evolutionary views.

He hoped that Lyell would undertake this weighty assignment. However, Lyell's *Antiquity of Man*, which came out in 1863, hedged, saying only: "If it should ever be rendered highly probable that species change

by variation and natural selection . . ." Darwin was
acutely disappointed, and all the more so because his
close friend was far bolder in conversation and correspondence. Darwin let his feelings spill out in letters to
Hooker. Lyell explained later that he did not want to
"dogmatize about the descent of man from the brutes,"
though he was prepared to accept the unwelcome fact. It
was some years before he revised his book to accept the
Darwinian thesis in full.

Perhaps, then, Wallace could be persuaded to write
the book on man. Wallace had been profoundly appreciative of Darwin's unselfish action in the remarkable
coincidence of their work on species, and Darwin felt
that Wallace's attitude was one of true nobility. The
relationship of these two men, both of whom had arrived
at the same ideas at approximately the same time, is one
of the most heart-warming and generous in the history of
science. Darwin once wrote to Wallace: "Your modesty
and candour are far from new to me. I hope it is a satisfaction to you to reflect—and very few things in my life
have been more satisfactory to me—that we have never
felt any jealousy toward each other, though in one sense
rivals. I believe that I can say this of myself with truth,
and I am absolutely sure it is true of you."

Wallace had previously prepared a brief essay on
man, which he had almost as a matter of course sent to
Darwin. In it he made some reference to the theory of
evolution as Darwin's. Before commenting on any other
point, Darwin quickly corrected this: "It is as much
yours as mine." Darwin suggested that Wallace might be
interested in following up his excellent essay with a
book, and if so, he had collected a few notes that he did
not suppose he himself would ever use. Characteris-

tically he added that he did not know if they were of any
value, and that they were in a state of chaos, but if Wallace should care to have them— Wallace said that he
would be glad to have the notes if he ever went on with
the subject. The "if" seemed most uncertain, and it
looked as though Darwin would have to do the work
himself if it were going to be done.

Darwin was not too reluctant. The case in the late
1860's wore an entirely different aspect than in 1859 or
earlier. When a naturalist like Carl Vogt could say in his
presidential address at the National Institution of Geneva
in 1869: "No one, in Europe at least, would dare to
maintain any longer that species were independently
created," it was manifest that a large number of naturalists, and particularly the younger ones, were admitting
that species were the modified descendants of other species. It was true that the "older and honoured chiefs" still
were opposed to evolution in every form, and that others
still insisted that man's origin could never be known, but
Darwin felt that he had enough acceptance to turn to the
critical subject. He argued the point in letters.

Darwin laid out all his voluminous notes. He wanted
to see first how far the conclusions he had arrived at in
the *Origin* and his other work applied to man. Besides,
he had not up to that time applied these principles to any
single species. To do so would be a most interesting
undertaking, he said.

In February 1867 the manuscript of *Animals and
Plants* had gone to the publisher. Before the proofs came
in, Darwin had a little free time, and he was so eager
to get to man that he began a chapter. As his books
tended to do, it began to grow in his hands, and soon
he was thinking of it as a small volume.

If man had descended from some "earlier and lower form"—Darwin's first proposition—then man should show plain traces of his ancestry. Were such signs evident?

Darwin turned first to the question of bodily structure. Bone for bone, muscle for muscle, nerve for nerve, man could be compared with the "monkey, bat, or seal" or any other mammal. And there were other points of correspondence not so evident. The fact that man can take certain diseases from animals, such as hydrophobia, and transmit others to them, certainly indicated a strong similarity of tissues and blood.

It was also convincing, Darwin pointed out as he marshaled his evidence, that the wounds of both are repaired by the same process and that reproduction is strikingly the same from the first act of courtship by the male to the birth and nurturing of the young.

There was another class of evidence, strange, eerie, and utterly inexplicable on any grounds other than an ancient community of descent. Man, Darwin showed, develops from an ovule, 1/125 inch in diameter, which differs in no respect from the ovules of other animals. And at various stages of his embryonic growth he develops gill-like openings in the neck, a hairy covering, and a tail, the os coccyx.

Long after birth man bears within him telling evidence of his ancestry. He has a long list of rudimentary muscles which are of no use to him in his modern life, but which were valuable to some of his ancestors. The appendix and wisdom teeth, Darwin noted, are such leftovers of the past.

To Darwin it seemed that the bearing of these three great classes of fact, structural, embryonic, and vestigial, was unmistakable. All were intelligible only "if we admit descent from a common progenitor." Man, Darwin argued, ought to admit frankly this community of descent. "It is only our natural prejudice and arrogance which made our forefathers declare that they were descended from demi-gods and which leads us to demur to this conclusion," he said in *The Descent of Man*.

This brought the naturalist to the second big question that he thought had to be applied to man: does each individual vary? The answer, of course, was an unhesitant yes. But the answer only raised another question, why? As to why men varied so extremely, Darwin could only say that "we are in all cases very ignorant."

He rather thought that use and disuse might be a factor in it. It was well known that if one kidney was destroyed by disease, the other increased in size and took over the full function. There seemed little doubt either that engravers tended to be nearsighted, and men living in the open, and particularly savages, farsighted. Whether such modifications would become hereditary if the same habits of life were followed for many generations was unknown, and yet Darwin concluded that it was probable they would be. His acceptance of this prevailing Lamarckian view was reluctant and begrudging, but he did accept it. Years later when the laws of genetics became known and it was proved that the effects of use and disuse are not heritable, Darwin's work was seriously discredited because of his partial yielding on this point.

Although Darwin could not say why man varied, he had no difficulty, as he continued the building of his case, in showing that man, like all other species, has a tendency to increase, and that he, like all other living things, must struggle for survival. The best-fitted to cope with the inexorable demands of life were on the whole those who survived and left offspring to succeed them. It was exactly as with other species.

Darwin could picture, in part at least, how the on-going and relentless process of natural selection might have turned some primitive ancestor into man as he exists in the modern world. This was plunging into a wholly new territory, but perhaps, Darwin said, some ancient member of the great series of primates became less arboreal. Perhaps some change in his food or sur-roundings led him to come down out of the green safety of the trees and take up life on the wide ranges of the ground. There it would have been a great advantage to him to walk on two legs—if his hands did not have to be used for locomotion, they would be free to manipu-late tools for fending off his enemies or killing his food. The animals which were the most bipedal and the most erect thus would have succeeded best, and probably would have left the largest number of progeny.

Once man's earliest ancestors were able to walk up-right, Darwin pointed out, other changes in structure would have to follow. The pelvis would have to be broadened, the spine "peculiarly curved," and the head fixed in an altered position, "all of which changes have been attained by man." Although he examined every phase of his problem, Darwin could find no scientific obstacles that would have barred man's acquiring his special and remarkable appearance. Man's physical structure could be accounted for.

Darwin's carefully buttressed argument—that man's bodily build testifies to his descent—was difficult to dis-pute. Many felt compelled to grant it. But a number of his critics, then and now, insisted that man differs so greatly from all other animals in his mental powers that he must be considered as of another kind.

Darwin had no inclination to avoid this serious objection. It was always his practice, as he worked, to seek out every opposing argument or objection. In this he followed what he liked to call a "golden rule": whenever he came upon a counter fact he made a note of it "because such facts are far more apt to escape from the memory than favourable ones." Therefore Darwin met frontally the strongest of all attacks made on his theory— the insistence that there is an unbridgeable difference in kind between man and ape.

He conceded at once that the difference between the lowest savage and the most highly organized ape is enormous. But so, he added, is the difference between the savage who cannot express any number higher than four and a Newton or a Shakspere. Both differences, Darwin set out to prove, are matters of degree.

His first point was that the lower animals as well as man feel pleasure, pain, happiness, and misery, and express these emotions in much the same way as man. In terror the muscles tremble, the heart palpitates, and the hair stands on end. Darwin also was convinced that man is not alone in experiencing what he called the more complex and "intellectual" emotions.

Darwin had heard that monkeys, despite their great dread of snakes, were unable to resist peering into a box where snakes were kept. He was so much surprised that he asked the zoological gardens to let him test the story.

Darwin walked into the monkey house carrying a stuffed snake. Most of the monkeys dashed around the cage, uttering sharp cries of alarm. When he laid it on the floor, however, they soon gathered around it, staring intently and "presenting a most ludicrous appearance." Darwin tried them next with a dead fish, a mouse, and a turtle. At first they were a little frightened, but before long they approached and were handling all three. He then brought in a closed paper bag containing a small live snake, placed it on the floor, and stepped back to see what would happen. One of the monkeys came up at once, cautiously opened the bag, peeked in, and dashed away wildly. And then monkey after monkey, with head held high and turned to one side, took a momentary peek at the dreadful object lying quietly at the bottom of the paper bag. They could not, Darwin said, "resist satiating their horror in the most human fashion."

There were others willing to grant all these points— that man and the higher animals have many of the same senses, intuitions, sensations, and faculties—but who argued that the final dividing-line, the line that can never be passed, is language. No animal other than man can put together a simple declarative sentence.

Darwin again answered analytically in the *Descent*. Many animals use sound to express their meaning. Any dog-owner, Darwin noted, knows the bark of eagerness, the howl of despair, or the note of supplication for a door to be opened. And certainly man too uses inarticulate cries, aided by gestures, to express his meaning. No sound is more expressive or more instantly understood than the quick cry of pain or surprise or the murmur of a mother to her beloved child.

Nor, Darwin continued, is the understanding of articulate sound or mere articulation itself a faculty of

man alone, for dogs can understand many words and
parrots and other birds can speak and even connect
words with events. Darwin's old friend of the *Beagle*,
now Admiral Sir B. J. Sulivan, had written him about
a parrot owned by his father. It always said "good morning" to everyone at breakfast, and "good night" at night,
and it never mixed the salutations.

"The lower animals differ from man solely in his almost infinitely larger power of associating together the
most diversified sounds and ideas; this obviously depends on the high development of his mental powers,"
Darwin wrote.

Darwin additionally shocked religious groups by
maintaining, though with gentleness and his own deep
reverence, that man's moral sense and conscience are not
a gift apart. These "most noble attributes" of man, he
declared, would develop inevitably as soon as the intellectual powers became as advanced as they are in man.
Darwin wondered that anyone would deny that the moral
sense might gradually evolve when "we daily see these
faculties developing in every infant."

The claim that man's highest qualities—his intellect,
his conscience, and his moral sense—could be a high
development of certain animal instincts and actions stood
in antipodal contrast to the prevailing ideas of the day.
The Duke of Argyll had expressed the general belief
when he said in his *Primeval Man*, a book published in
1869, that man came into the world a civilized being.
Savages, to this school, were men who had undergone
degradation and lapsed into barbarism.

"To believe that man aboriginally was civilized and
then suffered utter degradation is to take a pitiably low
view of human nature," Darwin pleaded in the *Descent*.

"It is apparently a truer and more cheerful view . . .
that man has arisen though by slow and interrupted steps
from a lowly condition to the highest standard as yet
attained by him in knowledge, morals and religion."

The pedigree that Darwin had given man had prodi-
gious length; it was not, he sorrowfully admitted, of
"noble quality." But Darwin felt that the human race
had no cause to be ashamed of it; "the most humble
organism is something much higher than the inorganic
dust under our feet; and no one with an unbiased mind
can study any creature, however humble, without being
struck with enthusiasm at its marvellous structure and
properties."

For many years as he gathered his notes on man and
worked on related subjects, Darwin had been troubled
by the fact that there were some differences between the
various races of animals and men which could not be
accounted for by natural selection alone.

Natural selection could not, for example, explain the
exquisite shading of the ball-and-socket ornaments on
the wing feathers of the Argus pheasant. In no way that
Darwin could see did the decorative spots give the male
pheasant an advantage in the usual struggle for life. Darwin also had to admit that the secondary sexual characteristics possessed by the males of most species—their
greater size, pugnacity, gaudy coloring, and weapons of
offense—served only to give one male an advantage over
another. Unless some other factor entered in, the less
showy males would succeed as well as the most brilliant in pairing with the females and leaving offspring.
Darwin cheerfully began a study of colossal proportions
to determine how another kind of selection could come
into play and affect the grand functioning of life. It was

thus that he was drawn into the subject that he called sexual selection.

As consistent material piled up in his portfolios on the structures, habits, and sexual differences of the upper groups of the animal kingdom, Darwin saw that if one individual of one sex were to prefer pairing with certain individuals of the other sex which were "characterized in some peculiar manner," their progeny would slowly but surely be modified in the preferred way. Thus if the female Argus pheasant through generations had chosen the most brilliantly ornamented males for her mates, it would be possible to explain how simple little spots with a tawny shading on one side might have evolved by small steps into the intricate and beautiful ball-and-socket ornaments. It was another kind of selection at work.

Darwin pointed up the distinction between natural selection and sexual selection. The latter depended on the success of certain individuals over others of the same sex. Natural selection depended on the success of both sexes in surviving the hazards of life.

His work on man drew Darwin deeper into this "hobby-horse" subject, for he felt certain, he said, that sexual selection had played a part in the formation of the various races of men. It was for this reason too that he felt justified in making sexual selection a second section of the *Descent*.

The "little volume" on man remained that; it was a brief six chapters. The section on sexual selection, however, expanded into fourteen voluminous chapters, packed with detailed observations on the sexual differences, the love antics, and the special characteristics of the crustaceans, insects, fish, birds, reptiles, and mammals. As Wallace said in a review, this was really a second book.

Darwin was tired and sick as he finished his second-greatest book, *The Descent of Man and Selection in Relation to Sex.* Knowing that it would bring new attacks, he wearily explained that he had not attempted to deal with the hopes and fears of the race, but only with the truth in so far as reason permitted him to discover it. "I have given the evidence to the best of my ability," he said.

The work had taken three years, including many interruptions because of prolonged bouts of headache and nausea. In the exhaustion and uncertainty of sending off the manuscript, Darwin complained to friends that the effort of writing the book had "half-killed" him, and that he had not the most remote idea whether it was worth publishing at all.

The *Descent* came out on February 24, 1871. The first edition of twenty-one hundred copies was quickly snatched up and a second of five thousand was ordered. Before long Darwin received £1,470 for his work, which he thought "a fine big sum."

Fed by the new and potent fuel in the *Descent*, the opposition to Darwin's views flared ever higher. But this time, as the *Edinburgh Review* pointed out, a few more expressions of "wonder and admiration" accompanied the wrath. *The Times* made up for its liberality on the *Origin* by printing a six-column article of stern disapproval. The conservative reviewer thought it lamentable that Darwin should have cast new doubt on man's God-given status at the very moment when the Paris Commune had been established and strange new ideas were spreading in England. Oxford and Cambridge had just been thrown open to all, regardless of religious belief. It was a further disturbing sign of the times that Parliament had yielded to long agitation and set up free primary schools, and that legislation was pending to charter trade unions.

Much as John Stuart Mill had advocated in his *Subjection of Women*, which had been published two years earlier, women's schools were being improved, and the Married Women's Property Act had permitted married women to retain control of their own money. Some women were even demanding the vote. To the reviewer it was not an appropriate moment for Darwin to rock the boat again.

Darwin was never happy about attack or comfortable under it. He took satisfaction, though, from the fact that the *Descent* was selling well. "The book has had a large sale," he wrote to one of his admiring German correspondents, "but I have been much abused for it, especially for the chapter on moral sense; and most of the critics consider the book as a poor affair. God knows what its merit may really be, all I know is that I did my best."

In combination with the *Origin*, this much-abused book became one of the most influential ever written. That was the verdict of history.

NINE

ALL IS CHANGED

DARWIN felt that his major work was done. Despite the uproar and criticism that greeted *The Descent of Man*, a profound change had occurred in scientific thought. Most naturalists now admitted the "great principle of evolution," and even the opposition had shifted ground.

Not many opponents of evolution still maintained that all living species had miraculously sprung full-blown from the dust of the earth. But early in the 1870's "several eminent naturalists" came out with a modified theory: though they conceded that most living species had developed from other and earlier forms, they declared with great firmness that the "true" species from which the many had come were unquestionably independent creations.

To grant that most species had been produced by variation while refusing to extend the same view to other and slightly different forms seemed curiously inconsistent to Darwin. The naturalists did not pretend that they could say which were the created forms of life.

In the winter of 1871–2 Darwin was working on revisions for a sixth and popular-priced edition of the *Origin*, and he decided, under the circumstances, not to remove some questions he had addressed earlier to those who denied evolution. "Do they really believe that at innumerable periods in the earth's history certain elemental atoms have been commanded suddenly to flash into living tissue? Do they believe that at each supposed act of creation one individual or many were

produced? Were all the infinitely numerous kinds of
animals and plants created as eggs or seeds, or as full
grown, and in the case of mammals were they created
bearing the false marks of nourishment from the mother's
womb?"

Darwin had been much censured for these questions
and for several other sentences which also implied that
naturalists believed in the separate creation of each species. He added a sentence in the new edition saying that
he was retaining the questions and other material as a
"record of the former state of things."

"Undoubtedly this was the general belief when the
first edition of the present work appeared," he said in
the *Origin*. "I formerly spoke to many naturalists on the
subject of evolution, but they either were silent or expressed themselves so ambiguously that it was not easy
to understand their meaning. Now things are wholly
changed. . . ."

Things were wholly changed. This, perhaps, was as
close as Darwin ever would come to acknowledging
that his great battle was largely won and that most men
thereafter would look upon themselves and the world
in new terms and new relationships. Darwin felt then
that thinking mankind would accept the long, lucid history he had written for all life. And he had an innate
though largely unexpressed confidence that the facing
of the truth and reality would be ennobling. This came
out both in his letters and in his books.

In the conscious and subconscious security of this
faith and knowledge, Darwin at last could relax. He
told his friends that he would no longer engage in any
fundamental theorizing, especially on so difficult a subject as evolution. His given reason was that he had seen

others fall into rash speculation in their later years, and one could never tell at what point his own intellectual powers might begin to fade.

And he was feeling old, or so he said to himself and others. It was true that at sixty-three his long, full beard and his heavy eyebrows were white. The stoop in his shoulders had become more marked, and as he took his daily turns around the sand walk he often stopped to lean on the alpenstock-type stick that he carried.

In fact, however, the ten years that remained for him were among his best, physically and mentally. As he felt under less pressure his health improved considerably. He could work for longer periods of time, he was able to see more people, and he traveled about more than in any of the other years since he had settled in the quiet retreat of Down. What was more, he continued to do brilliant, original, and influential work. There was none of the predicted "fading."

During the 1870's many visitors made their way to still remote Down—students, the curious, and distinguished foreigners eager to meet the man whose greatness they recognized. One week alone brought three noted Germans. Haeckel had been in correspondence with Darwin for many years and was a strong and valued advocate of evolution in Germany. He was a highly welcome guest, "nice, hearty, and affectionate," but the always forthright Emma explained in a letter to one of the children that he bellowed out his bad English in such a voice that "he nearly deafened us." On the day following his departure the two other German professors arrived. Emma thought that she had never heard anything like the noise they made, and added: "We have been rather overdone with Germans this week."

In 1871 Henrietta married Richard Litchfield, a barrister who was one of the founders of the Working-men's College. It was hard for Darwin to realize that the little girl who used to sit so solemnly on his knee was leaving his home. In a note written to her on her honey-moon in Europe the tender feeling Darwin had for all his children stands out: "From your earliest years you have given me so much pleasure and happiness that you deserve all the happiness possible in return. . . . Well, it is an awful and astounding fact that you are married, and I shall miss you sadly." He urged Etty to keep her mother in mind as an example of what a wife should be, for then, he added: "Litchfield in future years will worship and not only love you as I worship our dear old mother. . . ."

During the summer Litchfield often would organize walking-parties for the singing class that he taught at the college. After his marriage to Etty, the Darwins invited the group to come to Down each summer. Henrietta said in her book *A Century of Family Letters* that the in-vitations were greatly valued and that between sixty and seventy nearly always went on the outing. "My father and mother's gracious welcome, an excellent tea on the lawns, wandering about in the garden and singing under the lime trees made a delightful day," she happily re-called.

Charles and Emma went fairly often, for them, to visit Henrietta and her husband at their home, 4 Bry-anston Street, London. There Darwin could feel as much at ease and as free to set his own schedule as at Down.

It was on another visit to London, this time to the home of Erasmus in Queen Anne Street, that their son

George arranged for one of the séances that then had all London agog. Rather a "largish" party gathered around Erasmus's dining-table. George Eliot kept joking and refusing to sit in the proper silence, but finally everyone was settled down, with George Darwin and Hensleigh Wedgwood holding the medium's hands and feet. It was "grand fun," Darwin thought; bells rang, fiery points jumped around, and there were sundry rappings and movements of the furniture.

"The Lord have mercy on us," he later wrote to Huxley "if we have to believe such rubbish." However, he urged Huxley to look in on one of the séances and was very pleased with the long skeptical account of it that his friend later wrote to him. "To my mind an enormous weight of evidence would be requisite to make one believe in anything beyond mere trickery," he commented in his reply to Huxley. "I am pleased to think that I declared to my family that the more I thought of all that had happened at Queen Anne Street, the more convinced I was that [the medium] managed to get the two men on each side of him to hold each other's hands, and that he was thus free to perform his antics."

A little later Charles let Emma and members of the family persuade him to take a house in London for a month. During this visit he found that Huxley was worn from overwork and worry about a lawsuit in which he had become involved. Since Huxley could not afford to take a rest, Lady Lyell suggested to Mrs. Darwin that a few of his friends might join in making him a gift that would enable him to get away for a while.

Darwin leaped at the idea and quietly helped to collect £2,100 from a few close friends. He then had to write the letter telling Huxley of the gift. He labored fearfully over it; how could he find exactly the right words to make Huxley understand the spirit in which the gift was offered? But at last the "awful" letter was done, and to Darwin's great joy Huxley accepted the gift with understanding and appreciation. Some time later Darwin also took a leading part in obtaining a civil pension for Wallace.

All the while, as Darwin said in his autobiography, scientific work continued to be his "chief enjoyment and sole employment." From 1872 on, that permitted him to take up some of his favorite "hobby-horses"—studies that he had been easily and pleasantly carrying along, on the expression of emotion in man and animals, on insect-eating plants, on the movement of plants, and on worms! Oddly assorted though it sounds, the miscellany in fact bore directly on his major problem. This work completed the record: it tied in loose ends, it made use of materials he had gathered, and it importantly strengthened Darwin's theory of evolution.

In maintaining in *The Descent of Man* that the difference between man and the lower animals is one of degree and not of kind, Darwin relied heavily on evidence that the lower animals experience the same emotions as man and express them in much the same way. He had studied the latter problem in particular and had a great accumulation of data that he originally intended to present in a separate chapter. When he saw, however, that he could not satisfactorily get it all into such a limited space, he made only a few essential points and decided to take the remainder up later in "a separate treatise."

As soon as the *Descent* was finished he began to pull his "expression" material together and to write the book

that he called *The Expression of the Emotions in Man
and Animals*. To obtain a clear picture of how emotion
is expressed, "independently of the common opinion,"
Darwin had closely observed "the dawn" of emotional
expression in his own children. He also studied the animals around him, had a physician "galvanize" the facial
muscles of an actor, and sent questionnaires all around
the world. A friend in charge of a large insane asylum
made additional observations for him.

Darwin saw very early that such evidence would be
important to him. His interest also was piqued by a statement in a respected textbook that the muscles of the face
were "especially created" for the expression of the various emotions. Darwin "could not at all agree" with that.
When William ("Mr. Hoddy Doddy") was born in
1839 his father anxiously but accurately made notes—
when the child screamed the eyes became suffused with
blood and the muscles around the eyes were contracted.
The contraction, plus the opening of the mouth for the
lusty yells Mr. Hoddy Doddy could produce, also
brought the muscles at the corners of the mouth into the
strongest action.

Before very long William Darwin, like most other
civilized humans, learned not to scream at every frustration, but Darwin saw that the contraction of the eye
and mouth muscles continued at the least unhappiness.
The former produced the oblique eyebrows and
wrinkled forehead that are everywhere recognized as an
expression of distress, and the latter the equally well-
known "down in the mouth" expression.

Darwin once was sitting opposite an old lady in a
railway carriage. He was surprised suddenly to see her
"depressores anguli oris"—mouth depressor muscles—

contract lightly yet decidedly. As the rest of her face had not changed, Darwin began to ask himself if he could have been wrong about the expression. At that moment the woman's eyes filled with tears. She did not give way to grief in so public a place, but the muscles over which she had no conscious control had reacted.

A few of the greatest artists and writers had understood this muscular play and its meaning, Darwin learned. The Greek sculptors had furrowed the forehead of Laocoön and Arretino, though they had carried the transverse furrows across the whole breadth of the forehead and thus had "committed a great anatomical mistake." Darwin thought, however, that these "wonderfully accurate observers" might intentionally have sacrificed truth for beauty. Perhaps accurate rectangular furrows might not have had a "grand appearance in marble."

One of the most expressive of the many animals Darwin studied was his own dog Bob. Bob's chief joy was to go walking with his master, and they always started off with Bob trotting a few steps in advance, head and tail both held high. But the moment Darwin turned into the path leading to the greenhouse, Bob's whole expression changed; his head and body drooped and he took on the appearance of hopeless, piteous dejection known to the entire family as "Bob's hothouse face." Although Darwin could never bear suffering in animals, he could not help being amused at Bob's misery over so slight a cause. Bob always got his walk after a little delay.

The point was that animals, as well as man, can tellingly express their feelings. "He who will look at a dog preparing to attack another dog or man, and at the same animal when caressing his master . . . will be forced to admit that the movements of [his] features and [his] gestures are almost as expressive as those of man," Darwin said at the end of his chapter on animals.

Darwin, in studying his problem in men, tried to reach many different parts of the world. Is astonishment expressed by the eyes and mouth being opened wide and by the eyebrows being raised? he asked. When a man is indignant or defiant, does he frown, hold his head and body erect, and clench his fists? Is laughter ever carried to such an extent as to bring tears to the eyes?

There were sixteen questions in all. As the answers came rolling in, they indicated that the expression of grief, joy, anger, and other emotions is very much the same in all men, regardless of their degree of civilization or where they live. Tears, a smile, and the flush of anger were apparently universal. To Darwin this meant additional support for his thesis that the various races of men have descended from a single parent stock "which must have been almost completely human in structure and to a large extent in mind before the period at which the races diverged from each other."

Writing the *Expression of Emotions* was relatively easy for Darwin, and it was published in the fall of 1872. Darwin remarked in his autobiography that 5,267 copies—a substantial number—were purchased immediately by dealers.

On the day after the last proofs were corrected, August 22, Darwin began work on another hobby, insectivorous plants. He had long been interested in this matter. In 1860 when he had been at Hartfield, resting from the rigors of writing the *Origin*, he had spent many a pleasant day wandering around the Sussex countryside. The glistening, tentacled leaves of the common sun-

dew, a plant that grew abundantly there, caught his
appreciative eye. He was surprised to see a number of
insects snared on the leaves.

As he looked closer still, it struck him that in fact
the plants were veritable insect-traps. One large leaf
alone was strewn with the remains of thirteen distinct
victims. The idea that a plant could seize and seemingly
devour living creatures captured Darwin's interest as
irretrievably as the plant did any insect which might
alight on it.

When he returned to Down, Darwin took a number
of the plants with him. Around the edges of the leaves
was a shaggy fringe of what were generally called fila-
ments; Darwin, as he understood more of their nature,
always called them tentacles. At the tip of each was a
sensitive gland and surrounding it was a drop of extremely viscid secretion. It was this little drop of fluid,
shining like dew in the sun, that gave the plant its name.

When even a tiny insect alighted on a leaf, the nearest
tentacle at once began to curve down over it, exactly
like a finger closing into the palm of the hand. Watching through a lens, Darwin saw this action begin within
ten seconds. The tentacle bent closer and closer until
it had completely imprisoned the luckless insect, an action that sometimes was finished in about one minute.

And then an amazing process followed. The inflect-
ing tentacle, Darwin observed, pushed its prey within
the reach of the next tentacle, which in turn closed
down over it. By a curious sort of rolling motion the insect was carried to the center of the leaf and held in-
escapably by the closed tentacles. All the while the
glands were secreting copiously, and the acid liquid ran
down into the center of the trap. There it literally began

to dissolve the captive. The sundew—or *Drosera*, to use its botanical name—acted like a "temporary stomach," for it first dissolved and then absorbed the "delicious soup" produced from its captured food. *Drosera*, Darwin mused, could be said to feed like an animal.

In from one to seven days, when the meal had been thoroughly digested, the tentacles opened out again, ready to lure another victim to destruction.

Darwin was so fascinated by this animal-plant that by working with it he could forget his worries about species. Emma was grateful for *Drosera*. She explained in a note to Lady Lyell: "Charles is too much given to anxiety, as you know, and his various experiments this summer have been a great blessing to him, as he can always interest himself about them. At present he is treating Drosera just like a living creature, and I suppose he hopes to end in proving it an animal."

Emma made no attempt to understand her husband's work fully, and she was speaking loosely, though she was not far wrong. The experiments Charles carried on for fifteen years certainly emphasized the animal-like character of *Drosera* and other insect-capturing plants.

Very early in his work Darwin had an inspiration. He suspected that it was nitrogenous substances that *Drosera* was after. On this theory he placed a tiny bit of roasted meat on one of the leaves. The tentacles almost literally grabbed it. The leaves reacted with the same quick avidity when he offered them bits of the white of eggs, and other nitrogenous material.

As he worked, Darwin was increasingly astounded at the smallness of the particle that would cause the tentacles to inflect, and he decided to see to how tiny a bit they would react. One fleck, a bit of woman's hair, only

8/1,000 inch in length and weighing only .000822 milligram, brought the tentacles into motion. It was doubtful that a single nerve in the human body could have detected or been affected by so minute a particle. Darwin placed on his tongue a bit of hair 1/50 inch in length and therefore many times larger than the mote to which *Drosera* had responded. He could not feel it at all.

"It appears to me that hardly any more remarkable fact has been observed in the vegetable kingdom," he said.

Drosera's digestion, Darwin found, was as powerful as its tentacles were sensitive. Forty-eight hours after one of the leaves had clamped down on a cube of roasted meat, Darwin gently pried it open and examined what was left of the bait. It then consisted of nothing but a minute central sphere surrounded by a thick envelope of transparent fluid. Darwin put this material under his microscope. In the center part the transverse striæ of the muscular fibers of the meat were quite distinct. In the surrounding fluid, however, the fibers were replaced by transverse lines of small dark points.

At the time he first saw this effect, Darwin said, he did not understand its meaning. Only later when he read Schiff's *Leçons physiologie de la digestion* was the mystery cleared up, and excitingly. This study of the human stomach demonstrated that the connective tissues of meat dissolve first, leaving the corpuscles strung out in the original order—these were Darwin's dark points. Finally the lines are broken up and the cells dissolve and disappear.

The fact intensely interesting to Darwin was that *Drosera*—a plant, ordinary sundew—digested insects by exactly the same process as the animal stomach did meat. What was more, the digestive secretions were markedly similar.

"There is a remarkable accordance in the power of digestion between the gastric juice of animals with its pepsin and hydrochloric acid and the secretion of Drosera with its ferment and acid belonging to the acetic series," Darwin concluded. "That a plant and an animal should pour forth the same or nearly the same complex secretion is a new and wonderful fact in physiology."

To Darwin it spoke again of the oneness of all life.

Insectivorous Plants was published in July 1875. It was received with considerable interest, which of course was gratifying to Darwin, but he took pleasure in this new botanical book for a second reason. "It has always pleased me," he explained in his autobiography, "to exalt plants in the scale of organized beings."

Darwin went right on with the plant work which he loved so thoroughly and which was so much easier for him than writing or general research. Some authorities long had maintained that the principal difference between plants and animals lay in the latter's greater power of movement. It was a point that of course interested Darwin. In the early 1860's a paper by his good friend Asa Gray on "The Coiling of the Tendrils of Plants" had caught Darwin's attention with its suggestion that plants too could move. Perhaps plants were again being underrated. He decided to investigate the problem, and before he finished studied more than a hundred widely different species. His greenhouse soon was so filled with green climbers he had to have more space. To provide it, the billiard room was converted into a new and larger study.

Darwin started his work with an *Echinocystis lobata*,

or wild cucumber. As he watched its growth, he discovered that the upper part of each branch was constantly and slowly twisting, making a circle in from one half to two hours. The tips sometimes would go around two or three times, and then at the same rate would untwist and twist in the opposite direction.

"Confounded" by this strange behavior, Darwin begged for some advice from Hooker: "I have been observing pretty carefully a little fact which has surprised me; and I want to know from you whether it seems new or odd to you, so just tell me whenever you write; it is a trifling fact, so do not answer on purpose."

In the early stages of this work, the dizziness and nausea that always troubled Darwin became so bad that for many weeks he was unable to leave his room. He had one of the plants brought up, and in watching its performance could almost forget his own discomfort. Darwin tied the plant in such a way that only a young internode, about one and three fourths inches in length, was left free. At first it did not seem to move, but the next morning Darwin marked its position and discovered that the little shoot made a revolution in nine hours. As it grew longer, it picked up speed, and by the time it had grown to three and a half inches Darwin could clock its circuits from his sofa. It completed thirty-seven revolutions before it became upright and ceased moving.

In this way Darwin learned that a tendril revolves until it strikes some object, which it then curls around and grasps. About an hour later the tender young shoot begins to contract. By growth the tissues become strong and durable, and the tendril's work is done—admirably done, Darwin said with enthusiasm.

Plants became climbers, Darwin felt sure, to reach

the light and expose a large surface of their leaves to its action and to the free air. He marveled at the efficiency of this solution. The climbers satisfied their essential needs with amazingly little expenditure of organized matter, in comparison to trees, which to achieve the same end must have a load of heavy branches supported by a heavy trunk. It was for this reason, Darwin explained in the book he was writing, that there are in all quarters of the world so many climbing plants belonging to so many different orders.

Darwin did not finish his studies of climbing plants and his book about them until 1875. The book, called *The Movements and Habits of Climbing Plants,* nevertheless left one important problem unsolved. It was impossible to account for climbing plants' having been developed in so many wholly different groups unless all plants possessed some slight power of movement of an analogous kind. To find out if this was the case required exacting and difficult work. Darwin gradually succeeded in doing it, and his findings formed the basis for *The Power of Movement in Plants,* which he published in 1880.

Plants, then, these remarkable plants, could move and eat almost like animals, and Darwin suspected that there also were similarities in reproduction. It was by pure accident that he stumbled on the latter idea. In some of his early studies of inheritance he once raised two beds of *Linaria vulgaris,* the common toadflax. One was the product of self-fertilization, and other of cross-fertilization. Darwin was surprised to see that the seedlings of the self-fertilized parentage were inferior in height and vigor and almost every other way. This seemed so incredible that he thought some error must have been made.

The next year, though, when he carried out a similar inheritance study of carnations and obtained exactly the same result, he was "thoroughly aroused." He determined to work on this particular point, and did for eleven years.

He found, as he had in his work with orchids, that endless complex and wonderful contrivances had been developed for transferring pollen from one plant to another and thus achieving cross-fertilization. He reported his highly original findings in *The Effects of Cross and Self Fertilisation*, which was published in the autumn of 1876.

In the same year he finished another book on the same general subject, *The Different Forms of Flowers on Plants of the same Species*. Botanists had never known why in some cases a single plant bears two or three different kinds of flowers. By some very ingenious work Darwin discovered that the different forms are related to one another almost like the male and female of ordinary unisexual animals. This was an adaptation, he explained, to insure cross-fertilization and thus fitness to survive. Cross-fertilization was the final goal of the structure of flowers.

None of his "little discoveries" ever pleased Darwin as much as making out the meaning of the heterostyled flowers, he said in his autobiography. It touched on major problems, for cross-fertilization played an important part in keeping species constant, and this, plus Darwin's other work in botany, a field in which he regarded himself as only a devoted amateur, remade many important concepts.

"The aphorism 'Nature abhors close fertilization' and the demonstration of the principle, belong to our age and to Mr. Darwin," wrote Asa Gray in *Nature* in 1874. "To have originated this, and also the principle of Natural Selection . . . and to have applied these principles to the system of nature, in such a manner as to make within a dozen years a deeper impression upon natural history than has been made since Linnaeus is ample title for one man's fame."

Others equally well qualified to judge considered Darwin the greatest botanist since Linnaeus. But such an idea did not even occur to Darwin himself. In thanking a German botanist who had made a complete listing of his botanical works, his utter modesty about his work was clearly revealed: "Nothing has surprised me more than to see in your historical sketch how much I myself have done on the subject, as it never before occurred to me to think of all my papers as a whole. But I do not doubt that your generous appreciation of the labours of others has led you to over-estimate what I have done."

Working with plants never tired Darwin, and his work was eased from 1876 on by the assistance of his son Frank. Francis had been trained as a physician, but had never practiced; he was more interested in botany. After the death of his young wife at the birth of their son Bernard, he and the baby came to live at Down. Frank served as his father's secretary, and the baby was a great joy to his grandparents. Bernard would cry to be taken on his grandfather's knee and "have the bright spots," little flashing points of light that Darwin made with his pocket magnifying-glass.

The other sons were by this time married and established in homes of their own. Although they were living away from Down, their ties to it never slackened. William was a banker, living in Southampton. George had become a professor of astronomy at Cambridge, and Horace also had settled there as a manufacturer of scientific instruments. Leonard was in the Army. But all came frequently to Down, as did their wives and children.

The wives literally were welcomed as daughters. Darwin's feeling toward them was mirrored in the letter he wrote to Sara Sedgwick when she became engaged to William: "I must tell you how deeply I rejoice over my son's good fortune. . . . Judging from my own experience life would be a most dreary blank without a dear wife to love with all one's soul. . . . I can say with absolute truth that no act or conduct of William has ever in his whole life caused me one minute's anxiety or disapproval. His temper is beautifully sweet and affectionate and he delights in doing little kindnesses. That you and he may be happy together is my strong desire, and I thank you from the bottom of my heart for having accepted him."

To Darwin it seemed that his sons were all that a father could desire. It a letter congratulating George on an honor that had come to him, he wrote: "Oh, Lord, what a set of sons I have, all doing wonders." And this was written long before George, Frank, and Horace were knighted, and before Frank was elected president of the British Association for the Advancement of Science and Leonard president of both the Eugenics Society and the Royal Geographical Society.

Gwen Raverat, in her delightful *Period Piece*, stopped at the end of her chapter on the "Five Uncles," Darwin's five sons, and asked seriously if she had made them "too good, too nice, too single-hearted to be true." She did not hesitate long, however; it was true, so true that they never seemed to her to belong to the crude, ordinary world. They had never got into trouble of any kind, they had all had honorable and even distinguished careers, they had never met anyone around them with anything but kindness and gentleness. As Mrs. Raverat saw it, there was never anything for them to revolt against: "My grandfather was so tolerant of their separate individualities, so broad-minded that there was no need for his sons to break away from him; and they lived all of their lives under his shadow with the background of the happiest possible home behind them." But Gwen Raverat thought the unalloyed happiness and security and affection that had been theirs was not good for children; perhaps a little abrasion and toughening up would have been helpful too.

Whether the children were away or at home, life at Down continued at its placid, ordered pace of work, rest, walks, reading, backgammon. In 1876 Charles, in a letter to Asa Gray, reported the tally in the running backgammon game: "Emma, poor creature, has won only 2,490 games, whilst I have won, Hurrah, Hurrah, 2,795 games!"

Sheltered though his life was, Darwin as a man of science could not escape all involvement in public scientific issues, and he made it clear that he did not wish to. When England was embroiled in a controversy over vivisection, he thought it his duty to speak out. No one ever had a greater horror of suffering. Darwin once jumped from his carriage to halt a man who was abusing a horse, and returned pale and shaken by the experience. His own coachman did not dare to use the whip on the horses when he was driving his employer. One visitor who was being driven to Down once urged the coachman to go faster and was told: "Why, if I had whipped the horse this much in driving Mr. Darwin he would have got out of the carriage and abused me well." But Darwin knew that physiology could advance only by experiments with animals, and he did not hesitate on so important an issue to say so in letters to *The Times* and to a Royal Commission. He even went to testify before the commission.

Along with his botanical work, Darwin turned during the late 1870's to still another of his hobbies— worms. The truly startling experimental work that he did on the plain, ordinary earthworm, and the book that he wrote in 1881, completed an investigation that he had started forty years before. One more thread that had been left dangling was thus picked up and woven into his great fabric of evolution, and, like all the others, it fitted into and strengthened the fabric.

Darwin's interest in worms was aroused shortly after his return from the voyage of the *Beagle*. On a stroll about the lawns of Maer, his uncle, Josiah Wedgwood, happened to comment on the large amount of earth that undoubtedly was being brought to the surface by worms. It was exactly the kind of remark to fascinate Charles Darwin.

The two of them went to examine a field near Maer which had been spread with quicklime in 1827. A hole they had dug showed bits of the lime lying at a level two and a half inches below the surface. Charles was convinced that it had been buried by the worms. He saw that as the castings which the worms brought to the surface were dissolved and spread over the field by the rains, they would gradually cover anything left on top of the ground.

Darwin set forth this unorthodox theory in a paper, which he presented before the Geological Society of London in 1837. Reaction was slow in coming. It was ten years before M. D'Archiac wrote critically about Darwin's "*singulière théorie*." More years went by before another writer, in the *Gardeners' Chronicle*, took up Darwin's theory and haughtily rejected it on the ground that worms were "incapable, because of their weakness and size," of accomplishing any such "stupendous feat." This was in 1869.

Darwin once more was "aroused," for this touched on one of the critical points in his whole approach to science. It challenged his underlying belief that slow, imperceptible change can move not only the soil, but worlds. In the introduction to his book on the worms, Darwin spoke of the issue with as much indignation as he ever displayed on paper: "Here we have an instance of that inability to sum up the effects of a continually recurring cause, which has so often retarded the progress of science."

In this mood Darwin decided that he would reopen the subject and pile up new evidence. He soon was counting the number of worm tracks per square inch on the walks around Down, and had plunged into a study of the life, habits, and anatomy of worms—few studies had been made of animals "so low in the scale of organization." He carried a number of pots of worms into his study and thereafter spent many a day and many a night watching and experimenting with them—"training the worms," as Emma said.

Some of the few available reports had indicated that worms are very sensitive to light. During the night Darwin would tiptoe up to the pots—avoiding making any vibrations—and shine a red or blue bull's-eye lantern on them. The worms were not in the least disturbed by this performance. When, however, Darwin used a lens to concentrate the light of a candle on them, they scurried into their holes "like a rabbit into its burrow."

Darwin also wanted to test the response of worms to sound and vibrations. He began by blowing a shrill whistle near their pots. This the worms ignored completely, as they did the loudest and deepest tones of a bassoon that Darwin had played near them. But Darwin still was not satisfied; he carried some of the pots into the drawing-room and placed them on the piano. When he struck the note of C in the bass clef, down into their burrows went the worms.

While the white-bearded scientist was tiptoeing around his study beaming light and blowing whistles at worms, he also was making new field studies of their cumulative work. Near Down was a field last plowed in 1841. It had then been so thickly covered with flints that everyone called it the "stony field." When the boys ran down its slopes, the rocks clattered after them. But by 1871 the turf was so thick a horse could gallop over it without striking a single spark from a flint. To anyone who, like Darwin, remembered the field as it had been thirty years before, the transformation was "wonderful," and it was the work of worms.

"Great" stones too would be buried, Darwin was convinced. To put his theory to the most severe test, he undertook the unusual exertion of making a trip to Stonehenge to see what had happened to the ancient stones there. As he examined them and ran measuring

rods through the thick turf that had built up around
some that had fallen, he found that the worms had filled
in all the hollow spaces on the lower sides of the stones
—worms like such shelter. At the same time the burrows
they had excavated under the huge druidical stones gave
way and the big blocks settled gently into the enclosing
earth. Darwin returned home with exact measurements
and figures to prove that even the immemorial stones
of Stonehenge were yielding to the worms.

And so had ancient civilizations. In 1876, when some
work was being done at Abinger Hall, the estate of
Lord Farrer, some Roman ruins were uncovered. Lord
Farrer had married the daughter of Hensleigh Wedgwood, and it was only natural that Darwin should be
notified of the discovery. Charles and Emma went to
Abinger Hall the next summer to be present when an
exploratory trench was dug. Several feet below the surface the diggers came upon a layer of concrete covered
with tesseræ, or small red Roman tiles. The tiles were
part of the floor of the atrium, or reception room, of a
Roman villa! For years the field had been plowed and
cultivated without anyone's suspecting that the ruins
lay just below the green surface.

It seemed almost impossible that the large villa could
have been buried by worms, and at first glance the concrete showed little evidence of their action. The next
morning, however, as Darwin examined the downtrod-
den earth beneath the tiles, he found seven places in
which it had been lifted up over worm burrows. On
the third morning Darwin and Lord Farrer counted
twenty-five burrows, and by suddenly moving the cakes
of earth that covered them, they saw four worms hastily
retreating. The worms had been continuously undermin-

ing the floors and walls and heaping fine earth upon them "during many centuries, perhaps for a thousand years."

Darwin calculated that in many parts of England more than ten tons of earth annually passed through the bodies of worms and was brought to the surface on each acre of land. That meant, he pointed out, that in the course of every few years the whole soil of England moved through the bodies of the humble worms; they tilled it, they sifted it, they mixed it, they enriched it.

"It is to be doubted whether there are many other animals which have played so important a role in the history of the world as have these lowly organized creatures," Darwin concluded with what was evidently deep-felt satisfaction.

"Go proud reasoner, and call the worm thy sister," Erasmus Darwin had written in his *Zoonomia* almost a century earlier. His grandson, by an improbable turn of fate, had given new meaning to his words. Charles Darwin was sure that few people would be interested in his book about the worms and their work. It was true, as one reviewer observed, that to most men the worm was nothing but a blind, deaf, dumb, senseless, and unpleasantly slimy annelid. To be told unexpectedly that this disdained creature was the maker of the soil and the burier of ancient civilizations was the stimulating kind of shock the world thoroughly enjoys. *The Formation of Vegetable Mould through the Action of Worms* was received, when it came out in 1881, with what struck Darwin as "laughable enthusiasm."

All through the decade of the 1870's and into the 1880's the honors came crowding in upon Darwin.

Many foreign scientific societies vied in electing him to membership. He was surprised, nevertheless, to be informed in 1878 that he had been chosen a member of the *botanical* section of the French Institute. In scientific circles it had long been considered something of a scandal that Darwin was being kept out of the French honorary group. An attempt had been made to elect him to the zoological section in 1872, but in anti-evolutionist France he received only fifteen out of forty-eight votes. An eminent member of the institute explained with a certain stiffness: "What has closed the door of the academy to Mr. Darwin is that the science of those of his books which have made his chief title to fame— the *Origin of Species* and still more the *Descent of Man* —is not science, but a mass of assertions and absolutely gratuitous hypotheses, often evidently fallacious. This kind of publication and these theories are a bad example, which a body which respects itself cannot encourage."

Darwin was amused therefore at getting in through the botanical door. To Asa Gray he wrote: "It is rather a good joke that I should be elected to the Botanical Section, as the extent of my knowledge is little more than that a daisy is a Compositous plant and a pea a Leguminous one."

There was no quibbling when Darwin was chosen a corresponding member of the Berlin Academy of Science, with the distinguished sponsorship of Helmholtz and Virchow. He also received the Bressa Prize from the Royal Academy of Turin, the Baly Medal of the Royal College of Physicians, and, on his birthday in 1877, two magnificently bound and illuminated volumes containing the photographs of one hundred and fifty-four Dutch and German scientists who wanted to do him honor.

Writing to Professor A. Van Bemmelen of the Neth-
erlands to express his appreciation of the latter gift, he
said gratefully: "I suppose that every worker at science
occasionally feels depressed, and doubts that what he
has published has been worth the labour it has cost him,
but for the few remaining years of my life, whenever I
want cheering, I will look at the portraits of my distinguished co-workers in the field of science and remember their generous sympathy."

There were many other honors, but topping them all
was the honorary LL.D. bestowed by his own university, his beloved Cambridge.

On the morning of the ceremony, November 17,
1877, the Senate house was filled to overflowing with
undergraduates, some of whom had climbed up on the
statues of Cambridge's great. As Darwin was ushered in,
wearing the traditional scarlet silk gown, the cheers were
deafening. Emma, sitting with her sons and daughters,
was afraid that Charles would be overcome by the emotion of the moment, but he sat "quite stout and smiling"
waiting for the appearance of the Vice Chancellor.

Some cords had been stretched from gallery to gallery in the handsome old room, and suddenly a toy
monkey was run out on one of them. There was a roar
of delight. Before a proctor could rush up to capture
it and put an end to the play, a large beribboned loop
also came dangling out on the cords. It was the missing
link!

The entrance of the Vice Chancellor in scarlet and
white fur, preceded by two mace-bearers, put an end to
the capering. Solemn words, acknowledging the great
scientific contributions of the white-bearded man sitting
so quietly on the platform, rang out across the silent

room. *"Tu vero, qui leges naturæ tam docte illustraveris, legum doctor nobis esto,"* proclaimed the orator.[1]

College officials, students, and old friends crowded around to extend their personal congratulations to the man their university had honored. When the Darwins could break away, a "magnificent" lunch was served in George's rooms, and afterward Charles, with Emma on his arm, walked through the college grounds, reliving again his fondly remembered student days. He did not feel able, though, to remain for the "resplendent dinner" given that night by the Philosophical Club.

At the dinner Huxley responded to the main toast by lightly chiding Cambridge for waiting to bestow its highest honor until it was "safe and superfluous." Then, choosing his words with the utmost deliberation, he told that learned assemblage: "From Aristotle's great summary of the biological knowledge of his time down to the present, there is nothing comparable to the *Origin of Species* as a connected survey of the phenomena of life permeated and vivified by a central idea."

There was nothing comparable to the *Origin of Species* as a connected survey of the phenomena of life! Huxley's only qualification was the phrase "down to the present," a phrase that has not yet had to be altered. Down to the present no other scientist has reached so far and so wide, no other searcher for the truth has so clearly illuminated the order and principles that underlie the otherwise unexplainable form and diversity of nature. Not even Freud or Einstein has made so much of the universe comprehensible to us. Darwin still stands alone.

There were of course gaps and inadequacies in the

[1] "You, who have so learnedly illustrated the laws of nature, are declared our doctor of laws."

vast work of Charles Darwin, for his subject, life itself,
forced him to deal comprehensively and specifically with
the whole of life—its origins, its development, its organization, its workings.

As time went on, some of the gaps were filled in;
most notably, more of the missing fossil links were
found. New work also disclosed and pointed up a grave
error—Darwin's acceptance, reluctant and partial though
it was, of use and disuse as a factor in heredity. And
other new findings for a while cast doubt on several of
Darwin's essential premises.

The first great question arose out of the work of de
Vries and his demonstration that the new is often born
full blown. New forms had suddenly appeared in the
golden evening primrose with which the Dutch botanist
experimented; they were not produced through a process of natural selection. This seemed a vital challenge
to Darwin's contention that new species mainly arise
through natural selection. Several decades of research
were necessary to resolve the apparent conflict. But in
the end it was learned that Darwin was right. Modern
science proved that de Vries's mutations produce the new
which keeps evolution from a stalemate, but that natural
selection determines which mutations are bred into the
stock and which are bred out, and that natural selection
is therefore, as Darwin held, the great molder of life.

Again as the science of genetics developed and it
was found that heredity is a matter of the combination
and recombination of normal and mutant genes, there
was doubt as to whether Darwin's theories could fit into
the new context. But research proved once more that
it is natural selection acting on the genetic changes in
man, animals, and plants that produces evolution. Mod-

ern genetics has not only upheld Darwin, it has made untenable all other theories so far offered. Julian Huxley in his *Evolution in Action* [2] summed up the modern view: "So far as we know now not only is natural selection inevitable, not only is it *an* effective agency of evolution, but it is *the* only effective agency of evolution. With the knowledge that has been amassed since Darwin's time it is no longer possible to believe that evolution is brought about through the so-called inheritance of acquired characters—the direct effect of use or disuse of organs, or of changes in the environment; or by the conscious or unconscious will of organisms; or through the operation of some mysterious vital force; or by any other inherent tendency."

Darwin was one of the few scientists who both stated a great principle of nature and did the work, the massive work, required to establish the proof of that principle. More often in science the filling in of the proof has come long afterward. It is a measure of his greatness that modern science bows to his insight and accuracy on both scores.

At the same time, Charles Darwin finally established man's right to question all the manifestations of the universe around him, to seek a natural explanation of the being and the distribution of animals and man and even of the complexities of human actions. Without this freedom, which existed only in a limited degree before him, modern science could not be.

As the 1880's opened, it was clear that T. H. Huxley in his Cambridge speech had accurately reflected the judgment of much of the scientific world. The theory of evolution had won scientific acceptance and respect.

[2] New York: Harper & Brothers; 1953.

Darwin, as an intelligent man, could not fail to be
aware of the extent of his victory, but his sense of wonder at any phenomenon had not lessened, nor had his
innate, complete modesty. He marveled at the world's
acceptance of his theory of evolution, he was surprised
and awed. He ended the brief autobiography, on which
he had worked intermittently for some years, with these
words: "With such moderate abilities as I possessed, it
is truly surprising that I should have influenced to a considerable extent the beliefs of scientific men on some important points."

During the winter of 1881–2 Darwin suffered several attacks of weakness; after one attack he barely made
his way in from the sand walk. He sensed that not much
time remained to him, for in acknowledging congratulations from a friend on his seventy-third birthday, February 12, he observed as dispassionately as though he
were noting a scientific fact: "my course is nearly run."

There were a few final days of illness, and then on a
gentle spring day, April 19, 1882, Charles Darwin died
quietly at Down.

The world's acclaim broke forth, warmly, widely,
unstintedly, personally, and with all the formal, official
notice a nation accords to one of its great, to one who
has augmented the national renown not for one generation but for all foreseeable time. *The Times* spoke for the
world when it declared him "beyond rivalry among the
men of today and side by side with two or three great
discoverers of the past."

Twenty members of Parliament addressed a letter to
the Dean of Westminster: "Very Rev. Sir: We hope
you will not think we are taking a liberty if we venture
to suggest that it would be acceptable to a very large

number of our fellow-countrymen of all classes and opinions that our illustrious countryman, Mr. Darwin, should be buried in Westminster Abbey."

From the national point of view, Sir John Lubbock urged in a letter to the Darwin family, it was "clearly right" that Charles Darwin should rest in the Abbey rather than in the soil of Down which he had loved so well. It was clearly right in the eyes of all.

On April 26th a great black-clad congregation gathered in the stately Abbey for what was both a farewell and a national ceremony. Among them, *The Times* reported, were "leaders of men and leaders of thought, political opponents, scientific co-workers, eminent discoverers and practitioners of the arts." France, Germany, Italy, Spain, and Russia sent official representatives, as did the universities and the learned societies. And Charles Darwin, who had lived so simply, so quietly, and so modestly, was borne to his grave not only by those about whom his life had been built—Hooker, Huxley, Wallace, and his neighbor Lubbock—but by the American Minister, James Russell Lowell; Canon Farrar; William Spottiswoode, President of the Royal Society; the Earl of Derby; the Duke of Devonshire; and the Duke of Argyll. Of all those who had been closest to him, only Emma was absent.

"Happy is the man who findeth wisdom and the man that getteth understanding," rang out the words of the first anthem.

And as Charles Darwin was laid to rest in a grave beside that of the great Newton, the choir prophetically sang: "Let his body be buried in peace, his name liveth evermore."

NOTE ON SOURCES

THE story of Charles Darwin's life is told very completely
in his own books, his letters, and his autobiography. Here
are not only the great theories that remade the thinking of
the world, but a rich picture of how Darwin arrived at his
ideas, of the way in which he worked, and of the quiet, re-
tired life that he led. It is primarily from this original material that this book is written.

Although Darwin's own books are discussed in the text,
it seems to me that a consolidated chronological list may be
a convenience in this note:

1839   *Journal and Remarks*, as Vol. III of Fitz-
           roy's *Narrative of the Surveying Voyages
           of Her Majesty's Ships 'Adventure' and
           'Beagle' between the years 1826 and
           1836, describing their examination of the
           Southern shores of South America, and the
           'Beagle's' circumnavigation of the globe.*
           A second edition, somewhat changed, ap-
           peared as a separate publication in 1845.
           A third edition, called *A Naturalist's Voy-
           age*, came out in 1860. In the United
           States the Journal was published under the
           title *The Voyage of the Beagle*.

1839–43   *Zoology of the Voyage of H.M.S. Beagle.*
           Edited and superintended by Charles Dar-
           win.

1842–6   Geological Observations
           Part I. *The Structure and Distribution of
               Coral Reefs*, 1842
           Part II. *Volcanic Islands*, 1844

Part III. *Geological Observations on South America*

Parts II and III were republished in one volume in 1876.

1851-4   Cirripedia. First and second volumes on Cirripedes (barnacles) and on fossil cirripedes.

1859   *On the Origin of Species by means of Natural Selection.* 2nd ed., 1860; 3rd ed., 1861; 4th ed., 1866; 5th ed., 1869; 6th, and last, ed., 1872.

1862   *On the various contrivances by which Orchids are fertilised by insects*

1868   *The Variation of Animals and Plants under Domestication.* 2 vols.

1871   *The Descent of Man, and Selection in Relation to Sex.* 2 vols. 2nd ed. in 1874 in one volume.

1872   *The Expression of the Emotions in Man and Animals*

1875   *Insectivorous Plants*

The Movements and Habits of Climbing Plants, 2nd ed. An earlier essay first appeared in the ninth volume of the *Journal of the Linnean Society.*

1876   Autobiography, written. First published in *Life and Letters of Charles Darwin* in 1887.

The Effects of Cross and Self Fertilisation in the Vegetable Kingdom

1877   *The different Forms of Flowers on Plants of the same Species*

1880   *The Power of Movement in Plants*

1881   *The Formation of Vegetable Mould, through the Action of Worms*

The Voyage of the Beagle, the *Origin,* and

the *Descent* may be obtained in several
inexpensive modern editions. To the
best of my belief, the other books are
out of print. Copies may often be found,
however, in secondhand-book shops.

Also essential to any study of Darwin are his letters, his
Beagle diary and notebooks, and recollections of him written by members of the family. These include:

The Life and Letters of Charles Darwin, 2 vols., edited by
   his son, Francis Darwin, and including both the autobiography and reminiscences of Darwin's everyday life
   by Francis Darwin. New York: Appleton; 1887.
More Letters of Charles Darwin, 2 vols., edited by Francis Darwin and A. C. Seward. London: Murray; 1903.
*Charles Darwin's Autobiography, With His Notes and
   Letters Depicting the Growth of the Origin of Species*,
   edited by Sir Francis Darwin. New York: Schuman;
   1950.
Emma Darwin, A Century of Family Letters, 2 vols., edited by her daughter Henrietta Litchfield. New York:
   Appleton; 1915.
Charles Darwin's Diary of the Voyage of H.M.S. Beagle,
   edited from the manuscript by Nora Barlow, Darwin's
   granddaughter. Cambridge: University Press; 1933.
Charles Darwin and the Voyage of the Beagle, Darwin's
   letters written on the voyage and his notebooks, edited
   and with an introduction by Nora Barlow. New York:
   Philosophical Library; 1946.
Period Piece, family reminiscences by Gwen Raverat, Darwin's granddaughter. New York: Norton; 1953.

There is also valuable contemporary material in the *Life
and Letters* volumes of Darwin's great friends and co-
workers, Sir Joseph Dalton Hooker, Sir Charles Lyell, and

Thomas Henry Huxley, and in the autobiography of Alfred Russel Wallace and the letters of Asa Gray.

Many biographies of Darwin have been written. The earliest, which came out within ten years of his death, lacked material that became available later. The most complete, careful, and straightforward is Geoffrey West's *Charles Darwin, a Portrait* (New Haven: Yale University Press; 1938). Others include *Charles Darwin and the Theory of Evolution*, by Henshaw Ward (New York: New Home Library; 1943, originally published in 1927); *Darwin*, by Gamaliel Bradford (Boston: Houghton Mifflin; 1926); and *The Evolution of Charles Darwin*, by George A. Dorsey (Garden City: Doubleday; 1927). *Charles Darwin—the Naturalist as a Cultural Force*, by Paul B. Sears (New York: Scribner's; 1950), is a fine study that is a biography as well as a specialized appraisal.

Innumerable books have discussed the theories of Charles Darwin and their effect on all the fields of modern thought and science. No attempt will be made to list them here.

A number of other books bring the story of evolution up to date. Julian Huxley's *Evolution in Action* (New York: Harper; 1953) and George Gaylord Simpson's *The Meaning of Evolution* (New Haven: Yale University Press; 1949) are fine, authoritative books, meaningful to the layman as well as the professional. Reference also is made to the author's *Man, Time, and Fossils* (New York: Knopf; 1953), which traces the effect on Darwin's theory of the work done by his followers from Mendel through the geneticists and on to the modern anthropologists and atomic physicists.

The *Autobiography* of Sir Arthur Keith (New York: Philosophical Library; 1950) tells of the successful fight to save Darwin's home, Down, as a national monument.

INDEX

This book was set on the Linotype in a face called *Eldorado*, so named by its designer, WILLIAM ADDISON DWIGGINS, as an echo of Spanish adventures in the Western World. The series of experiments that culminated in this type-face began in 1942; the designer was trying a page more "brunette" than the usual book type. "One wanted a face that should be sturdy, and yet not too mechanical. . . . Another desideratum was that the face should be narrowish, compact, and close fitted, for reasons of economy of materials." The specimen that started Dwiggins on his way was a type design used by the Spanish printer A. de Sancha at Madrid about 1774. Eldorado, however, is in no direct way a copy of that letter, though it does reflect the Madrid specimen in the anatomy of its arches, curves, and junctions. Of special interest in the lower-case letters are the stresses of color in the blunt, sturdy serifs, subtly counterbalanced by the emphatic weight of some of the terminal curves and finials. The roman capitals are relatively open, and winged with liberal serifs and an occasional festive touch.

This book was composed, printed, and bound by The Plimpton Press, Norwood, Massachusetts. The typography and binding were designed by the creator of its type-face—W. A. Dwiggins.